Second Edition

STUDENT ACTIVITIES

THE AMERICAN REPUBLIC

for Christian Schools®

TEACHER'S EDITION

Michael D. Matthews

Bob Jones University Press, Greenville, SC 29614

NOTE:
The fact that materials produced by other publishers are referred to in this volume does not constitute an endorsement by Bob Jones University Press of the content or theological position of materials produced by such publishers. The position of Bob Jones University Press, and the University itself, is well known. Any references and ancillary materials are listed as an aid to the student or the teacher and in an attempt to maintain the accepted academic standards of the publishing industry.

Student Activities in THE AMERICAN REPUBLIC for Christian Schools® Teacher's Edition Second Edition

Michael D. Matthews, M.Ed.

Composition by Nancy Lohr
Design by Joyce Landis
Cover by John Bjerk
Illustrations by Timothy Banks
Edited by Elizabeth B. Berg

Produced in cooperation with the Bob Jones University Department of History of the College of Arts and Science, the School of Religion, and Bob Jones Academy.

for Christian Schools is a registered trademark of Bob Jones University Press.

ISBN 1-57924-334-7

15 14 13 12 11 10 9 8 7 6 5 4 3 2

Contents

How to Use the Activities Manual

These activities are designed to give you maximum flexibility. We have provided a "menu" of activities from which you can select the ones that will help you achieve your instructional goals. Before you begin each chapter, look over the activities and decide how you want to assign them. The activity codes and skill codes at the bottom of each page will help you decide.

Activity Codes

Each chapter has two to six activities. The *activity* code tells you which sections of the chapter each activity covers. The code also tells you whether the activity is good for reinforcement, enrichment, or review.

- *Reinforcement* activities are based solely on the information in the textbook. They help students (1) to recognize and recall major terms and concepts in the chapter and (2) to "put it all together." Some reinforcement activities, such as charts and time lines, cover the entire chapter. (Students can complete them as they read through the chapter or as they review for tests.) Other reinforcement activities apply to a specific section of the chapter. (Students can complete them as they read the section.)

- *Enrichment* activities go beyond the textbook. They help students (1) to apply information from the chapter, (2) to pursue subjects they find interesting, and (3) to develop special skills. Every student can benefit from these activities, but they are particularly useful for students who need a challenge. Most enrichment activities are related to a specific section in the chapter.

- *Chapter review* activities help students to prepare for the chapter test. They include crossword puzzles, games, and other interesting activities that review the chapter.

Alternative Uses of the Activities

Activities are useful for more than just homework. You can make them an integral part of your classroom discussion. Your students will especially appreciate your help in completing the more difficult activities.

- Homework—The students complete the activity at home.

- Class activity—The students complete the activity in class by themselves or in groups.

- Class discussion—You help the class complete the activity together in a classroom discussion.

- Lecture—You complete the activity on the chalkboard or on the overhead projector during your lecture while the students take notes.

- Game—The students answer each question in a competition that pits team against team or "every man for himself."

Skill Codes

Every activity focuses on one of eighteen skills that history students need to learn. Some activities teach specific skills, such as mapping. Others teach basic thinking skills, such as recognizing terms. The activities for each skill increase in variety and difficulty over the year. The chart does not include four geography activities at the end of Chapters 3, 10, 16, and 20 or course review activities at the end of the book. *Note: Each letter in the chart below corresponds to the activity for that chapter.*

Chapter	1	2	3	4	5	6	7	8	9	10	11	12	13	14	15	16	17	18	19	20	21	22	23	24	25	26	27	28	29	30
1. Maps		B	A		A	A				A	A		A	D	A		A		B			A	E			D,E	C			
2. Charts	A	A	B		C		A	B,C			B		B	A	B	A		B	D		A	C	A	A	A	C	A			E
3. Outlining				A				A				A							B							B				
4. Time Line	B					B			A	C						B	A											A		
5. Graphs													C			C								C		C		A		
6. Original Sources	C			C	B				D	B		B		C																
7. Cause and Effect				D								C			C						C				A					
8. Using Resources											C						D		C	C				C						
9. Bible Study			B				B		E													B								C
10. Writing		D		D					F	D				D	B			A	A	B	B	C	E					B		A
11. Vocabulary					D				B															D						
12. Test Taking					E							C												F						
13. Recognition	D	C	D	F	C	C	D	D					E		E			B				D		C		F		C	C	
14. Comprehension		C				C							F		C					D				D		D				
15. Application					E			E						D										D					B	D
16. Analysis													D		B									B						B
17. Synthesis											D																	B		
18. Evaluation																	E					A			B			D		

Alternatives to Grading and Burdensome Records

You don't need to grade all the activities. You can complete some of them in class discussions, games, and lectures, as mentioned above. Or you can use some of the ideas below.

- Check marks—Give simple pluses and minuses. You can use this information to decide borderline grades or—if you use them—"effort" grades.
- Extra credit—Let students do activities for extra credit, if they wish.
- Sporadic grades—Grade every third or fourth activity, but do not let students know which activities will be graded.
- Notebook—Make students keep their activities in a notebook. Collect the notebooks quarterly and grade them for neatness, completeness, and accuracy.

SPECIAL NOTE ABOUT THE CLASS DISCUSSION ICON ☆

This icon signifies activities that assess students' general recall and comprehension. They give you an excellent opportunity to ask a series of thought-provoking questions. At least one student will usually have the answer. If everyone is stumped, then you can supply the answer from the teacher manual without extra work on the students' part. Only the most exceptional student, who relishes a challenge, will benefit from doing these time-consuming activities as homework.

American Republic

Chapter 1   Activity A

Explorers of a New World

Complete the chart. For each explorer write the country he served, the dates given in the textbook for his exploration, and his main accomplishment. Refer to the textbook (including the map on page 10) for your answers.

Explorer	Country	Dates	Main Accomplishment
Christopher Columbus	*Spain*	*1492*	*discovery of the New World* pp. 1, 4-5
John Cabot	England	1497-98	**English claim to North America's Atlantic coast** p. 10
Amerigo Vespucci	*Spain/ Portugal*	*1499/1501*	**proof that America was a "new world"** p. 5
Vasco de Balboa	Spain	1513	**crossing the Isthmus of Panama** p. 5
Ferdinand Magellan	Spain	1519-22	**first circumnavigation of the earth** p. 5
Hernando Cortés	Spain	1519	**conquest of the Aztecs in Mexico** p. 6
Francisco Pizarro	Spain	*1533*	**conquest of the Incas in Peru** pp. 3, 6
Jacques Cartier	France	1534	**discovery of the St. Lawrence River** pp. 9-10
Sir Francis Drake	England	1577	**second circumnavigation of the earth** p. 7
Robert de La Salle	France	1681-82	**French claim to the Mississippi River** p. 9

Answer these questions based on the chart.

1. Which was the first country to send an explorer to the New World? ___*Spain*___

2. Which was the last country to send an explorer to the New World? ___*France*___

3. Which explorer sailed for two different countries? ___*Amerigo Vespucci*___

4. How many years passed between the first and second circumnavigation? ___*about 55*___

5. How many years passed between the first and last exploration? ___*about 190*___

American Republic

Chapter 1   Activity B

Settlement of the New World

Arrange these events in the order in which they occurred.

Europeans began to desire the spices of the East.

The Line of Demarcation divided the New World between the Portuguese and the Spanish.

The House of Burgesses became America's first representative government.

Christopher Columbus landed at San Salvador.

John Smith helped to establish the Jamestown settlement.

The Viking Leif Ericson found "Vinland."

Robert de La Salle claimed the Mississippi River for France.

The Spanish conquistadors conquered the Aztecs and Incas.

The Mayas built stone pyramids.

An English "Sea Dog" helped defeat the Spanish Armada.

The Mayas built stone pyramids.   p. 2

The Viking Leif Ericson found "Vinland."   p. 3

Europeans began to desire the spices of the East.   p. 4

Christopher Columbus landed at San Salvador.   p. 1

The Line of Demarcation divided the New World between the Portuguese and the Spanish.   p. 6

The Spanish conquistadors conquered the Aztecs and Incas.   p. 6

An English "Sea Dog" helped defeat the Spanish Armada.   pp. 7-8

John Smith helped to establish the Jamestown settlement.   pp. 10-11

The House of Burgesses became America's first representative government.   p. 12

Robert de La Salle claimed the Mississippi River for France.   pp. 9-10 (map)

American Republic

Chapter 1   Activity C

Captain John Smith's Account of the Founding of Jamestown

John Smith wrote eight books about his adventures in the New World. After you read about the founding of Jamestown in Smith's own words, answer the questions that follow.

While the ships stayed, our allowance was somewhat bettered by a daily proportion of biscuit, which the sailers would pilfer to sell, give, or exchange with us, for money, sassafras, or charity. But when they left, there remained neither tavern, beer house, nor place of relief, but the common kettle. Had we been as free from all sins as gluttony and drunkenness, we might have been canonized for saints. But our president would never have been admitted, for he ingrossed for his private use oatmeal, white wine, oil, aqua vitae [brandy], beef, eggs, or what not. But the kettle that he allowed to be distributed was half a pint of wheat and as much barley boiled with water for a man a day; and this having fried some six weeks in the ship's hold, contained as many worms as grains. Our drink was water, our lodgings castles in the air.

With this lodging and diet, our extreme toil in bearing and planting palisades [fort posts] so strained and bruised us, and our continual labor in the extremity of the heat had so weakened us, and were sufficient cause to have made us as miserable in our native country or any other place in the world.

From May to September those that escaped lived upon sturgeon and sea-crabs. Fifty in this time we buried; the rest seeing that the president (who all this time had neither felt want nor sickness) planned to escape these miseries in our pinnance [small ship] deposed [him]. . . .

But now was all our provision spent, the sturgeon gone, all helps abandoned, each hour expecting the fury of the savages, when God the patron of all good endeavors, in that desperate extremity so changed the hearts of the savages that they brought so much of their fruits and provision that no man wanted for anything.

The new president and Martin, being little beloved, weak judgment in dangers, and less industrious in peace, committed the managing of all things abroad to Captain Smith who by his own example, good words, and fair promises, set some to mow, others to bind thatch, some to build houses, others to thatch them. He himself always bore the greatest task for his own share, so that in short time, he provided most of them with lodging, neglecting any for himself.

1. What was wrong with the colony's first president? ___*He was a glutton and a drunkard.*___

2. What is meant by "castles in the air"? ___*No one had a house.*___

3. How many men died during the first few months? ___*fifty*___

4. What did Smith call the Indians? ___*savages*___

5. How did God save the starving colonists? ___*The Indians gave them food.*___

6. What was wrong with the second president? ___*He was lazy and lacked common sense.*___

7. What was Smith's opinion of himself? ___*He was an outstanding leader.*___

8. List four hardships the colonists faced. ___*Choose four: starvation, exposure, heat, Indians,*___ ___*sickness, and bad leaders.*___

American Republic

Chapter 1   Activity D

Crossword Puzzle

Across

5. king of Spain in 1492 *p. 4*
6. person who drew the Line of Demarcation *p. 6*
7. Indian empire in Mexico *p. 3*
8. French Protestants *p. 9*
p. 10 13. the "_____ Colony" of Roanoke Island
14. Spanish term for "conqueror" *p. 5*
16. country that claimed the Mississippi River *p. 9*
p. 10 20. first English baby born in the New World
21. queen of England in 1588 *p. 7*
p. 11 23. colonist who introduced tobacco (initials)
p. 9 24. discoverer of the St. Lawrence (initials)
p. 8 25. country that defeated the Spanish Armada
26. country that divided the world with Portugal *p. 6*
27. England's first explorer (initials) *p. 10*
28. Indian "corn" *p. 2*

Down

1. Norsemen who colonized Greenland *p. 3*
2. Indians who built an empire in Peru *p. 3*
3. profitable money crop of Jamestown *p. 11*
4. tasty product of the Orient *p. 4*
9. Sir Francis Drake's ship *p. 7*
10. man who started the Reformation *p. 7*
11. Virginia's House of _____ *p. 12*
12. early leader of Jamestown (initials) *p. 11*
15. "constantly on the move" *p. 2*
17. Englishman whose colony failed *p. 10*
18. name of the New World in honor of Vespucci *p. 5*
19. wife of 5 across *p. 4*
22. legendary Welshman who settled in America *p. 3*

4   **Chapter Review**   **Skill: Recognition**

American Republic

Chapter 2   Activity A

Thirteen Different Colonies

Complete the chart (except for the shaded areas). Refer to the textbook (including the chart on page 17). The important leaders, first settlements, and facts of interest are listed below the chart.

Colony	Important Leaders	First Settlement	Date	Facts of Interest
Massachusetts	John Carver William Bradford John Winthrop	Plymouth (Salem)	1620 (1628)	Puritans, Separatists Mayflower Compact the Great Migration
New Hampshire		Odiorne's Point	1623	
Connecticut	Thomas Hooker p.23	Windsor	1633	Fundamental Orders p. 24
Rhode Island	Roger Williams p. 22	Providence	1636	
New York	Peter Minuit Duke of York p. 25	Albany	1624	originally New Netherland patroons p. 25
New Jersey	George Carteret John Berkeley p. 25			once a portion of New York p. 25
Delaware		Wilmington	1638	originally New Sweden p. 27
Pennsylvania	William Penn p. 26	Philadelphia	1682	Quaker "Holy Experiment" p. 26
Virginia	John Rolfe p. 28	Jamestown	1607	tobacco p. 28
Maryland	George Calvert Cecilius Calvert p. 30	St. Marys	1633	colony for Roman Catholics Act of Toleration p. 30
North Carolina		Albermarle Sound	1654	
South Carolina		Charleston	1670	indigo and rice p. 31
Georgia	James Oglethorpe p. 31	Savannah	1733	debtors' colony pp. 31-32

Leaders	Settlements	Facts
John Berkeley	Albany	Act of Toleration
Cecilius Calvert	Albermarle Sound	colony for Roman Catholics
George Calvert	Charleston	debtors' colony
George Carteret	Jamestown	Fundamental Orders
Duke of York	Odiorne's Point	indigo and rice
Thomas Hooker	Philadelphia	once a portion of New York
Peter Minuit	Providence	originally New Netherland
James Oglethorpe	Savannah	originally New Sweden
William Penn	St. Marys	patroons
John Rolfe	Wilmington	Quaker "Holy Experiment"
Roger Williams	Windsor	tobacco

American Republic

Chapter 2   Activity B

Map Study: The Original Colonies

Refer to the maps in the textbook on pages 24, 26, and 30 to complete the map below.

Students must place their own dots for cities. Encourage them to write words in the margin and draw lines to the location, as in the textbook.

1. Label each of the thirteen colonies.

2. Using three colored pencils, color the key and the corresponding regions on the map.

3. Label these settlements: Jamestown, Plymouth, Salem, Boston, Providence, Albany, Philadelphia, Charleston, and Savannah.

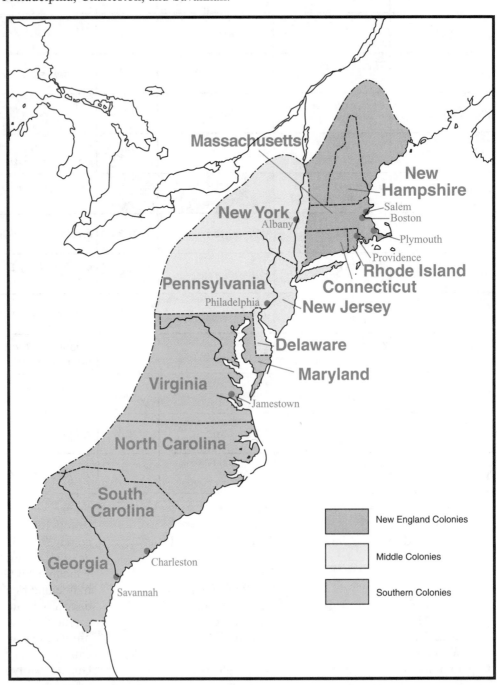

American Republic

Chapter 2   Activity C

Mystery Colony

See text p. 21 and Matthew 5:14.

Jesus told his disciples that something "cannot be hid." To find out what cannot be hidden, complete the puzzle below. What colony adopted this phrase as its theme?

1. What do we call the landholders who brought at least fifty settlers to New Netherland? *p. 25*
2. What official document gave each joint-stock company permission for founding a colony? *pp. 16-17*
3. What type of business raised large sums of money by selling "shares of stock"? *p. 16*
4. What town in Connecticut did Thomas Hooker found in 1636? *p. 23*
5. What type of colony fell under the direct supervision of the king? *p. 17*
6. Who received a large grant in the New World from his brother, the king of England? *p. 25*
7. What do we call the Separatists who founded Plymouth? *p. 18*
8. What type of colonial organization did Pennsylvania have? *pp. 17 (chart), 26*
9. What country did the Pennsylvania Dutch come from? *p. 27*
10. What Indian showed the colonists at Plymouth how to plant corn? *p. 19*
11. What church did the Puritans want to "purify"? *p. 18*
12. What crop was commonly used to make a blue dye? *p. 31*
13. What colonial city became the largest in America? *p. 27*
14. What colony did William Bradford lead? *p. 19*

```
 1.      P  A  T  R  O  O  N  S
 2.         C  H  A  R  T  E  R
 3.      J  O  I  N  T  -  S  T  O  C  K
 4.      H  A  R  T  F  O  R  D
 5.      R  O  Y  A  L
 6.      D  U  K  E     O  F     Y  O  R  K
 7.         P  I  L  G  R  I  M  S
 8.      P  R  O  P  R  I  E  T  A  R  Y
 9.  G  E  R  M  A  N  Y
10.      S  Q  U  A  N  T  O
11.  C  H  U  R  C  H     O  F     E  N  G  L  A  N  D
12.         I  N  D  I  G  O
13.   P  H  I  L  A  D  E  L  P  H  I  A
14.      P  L  Y  M  O  U  T  H
```

15. What is the name of the mystery colony? _____ *Massachusetts Bay Colony* _____

American Republic

Chapter 2   Activity D

Founding Your Own Colony

The year is 1580. You are a young English nobleman who has just inherited one million pounds (a lot of money)! The king has asked you to found a colony anywhere on the coast of North America. You need to answer these questions as you make preparations to settle your colony. Can you avoid the costly mistakes that other colonists made?

1. How do you plan to attract people to your colony? Check at least one attraction.
   ❑ profit ❑ employment ❑ political freedom
   ❑ land ownership ❑ religious freedom ❑ adventure

2. What kind of colony will you have?
   ❑ charter colony ❑ proprietary colony ❑ royal colony

3. Which feature will determine where your colony will be?
   ❑ good harbor ❑ gold ❑ navigable river
   ❑ furs ❑ climate ❑ soil
   ❑ safety ❑ nearby Indians ❑ woods

4. Which region will have the best site for your colony?
   ❑ New England ❑ middle region ❑ southern region

5. What difficulties is your colony likely to face?
   ❑ famine ❑ bad weather ❑ Indian attack
   ❑ disease ❑ poor leadership ❑ bankruptcy
   ❑ lazy settlers

6. How will the colony pay for itself?
   ❑ mining ❑ shipbuilding ❑ tobacco
   ❑ fur trade ❑ gifts from the king ❑ indigo
   ❑ sale of lands ❑ fishing ❑ rice

7. What basic supplies will you need? Place an *x* in the boxes beside items you will need to bring only once, and fill in boxes beside items you will need to resupply from England.
   ❑ seeds ❑ guns ❑ tools/instruments
   ❑ flour ❑ boats ❑ candles/lanterns
   ❑ salt ❑ money ❑ _____
   ❑ meat ❑ paper/ink ❑ _____
   ❑ fresh water ❑ clothes/linen ❑ _____

8. Whom must you bring along on your first trip? Check the ten most important occupations. You may need to use a dictionary. Be ready to defend your choices.
   ❑ smith ❑ husbandman ❑ weaver
   ❑ shipwright ❑ carpenter ❑ salt maker
   ❑ cooper ❑ divine ❑ sturgeon dresser
   ❑ baker ❑ mason ❑ fisherman
   ❑ sawyer ❑ soldier ❑ physician
   ❑ miner ❑ fowler ❑ tailor

9. What historical figure would you like to lead your colony? Explain why.
   - ❑ John Rolfe
   - ❑ John Carver
   - ❑ Roger Williams
   - ❑ William Penn
   - ❑ John Smith
   - ❑ William Bradford
   - ❑ Thomas Hooker
   - ❑ Cecilius Calvert
   - ❑ Sir Walter Raleigh
   - ❑ John Winthrop
   - ❑ Peter Minuit
   - ❑ James Oglethorpe

   _____

   _____

10. Write a brief summary of the first three years of your colony. (Your account may be very short if your colonists all disappear, die, or decide to return to England.) Mention the major accomplishments and setbacks during each time period (completing the fort, finishing the houses, harvesting the first crop, arrival of a supply ship, etc.).

    First Month

    _____

    _____

    _____

    First Six Months

    _____

    _____

    _____

    First Year

    _____

    _____

    _____

    _____

    Second Year

    _____

    _____

    _____

    Third Year

    _____

    _____

    _____

    _____

Skill: Writing

American Republic

Map Study: The North Atlantic Coast

Refer to the physical map in the textbook on page 35 to complete the map below.

1. Label these rivers:
   Hudson
   Delaware
   Susquehanna
   James
   Santee
   Savannah
   Allegheny

2. Label these bays:
   Massachusetts
   Delaware
   Chesapeake

3. Label these land features:
   coastal plain
   Piedmont
   Appalachian Mountains

4. Label these settlements:
   Albany
   Boston
   Nantucket
   New Bedford
   New York
   Philadelphia
   Williamsburg
   Jamestown
   Charleston

5. Draw these figures beside the appropriate settlements:

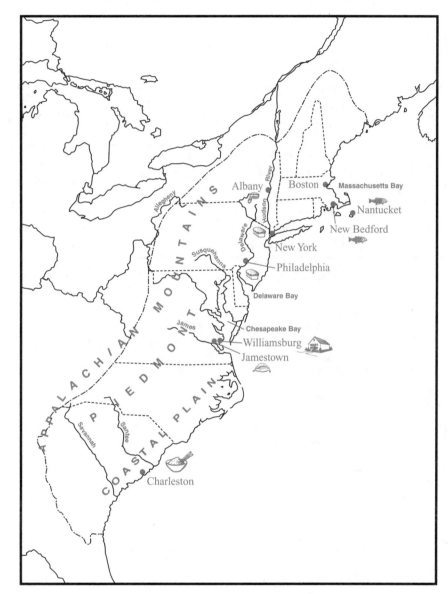

 two whaling ports   *p. 36*

 fur-trading center   *p. 38*

 two breadbasket ports
      pp. 35 (map), 37

 first tobacco port   *p. 38*

 rice port   *pp. 35 (map), 38*

 first legislature—House of Burgesses
      p. 45

Reinforcement: Section 1   Skill: Maps   **11**

American Republic

Chapter 3   Activity B

Early Colonial Differences    *Classroom discussion*

Complete the chart (except for the shaded areas). The answers are listed below the chart. Some spaces have more than one answer.

	New England	Middle Colonies	Southern Colonies	Frontier
Occupations	*fishing/whaling shipbuilding p. 36*	*bread colonies fur trade pp. 37-38*	*plantations p. 38*	*subsistence farming*
Physical Features	*hilly thin, rocky soil p. 36*	*navigable rivers rich, thick soil p. 37*	*wide coastal plain tidewater p. 38*	*Appalachian Mountains*
Main Ports	*Boston Nantucket New Bedford p. 36*	*Philadelphia p. 37*	*Jamestown Charleston Savannah p. 35 (map)*	
Settlers	*mostly English p. 37*	*melting pot p. 37*	*mostly English p. 38*	*variety/riffraff*
Aristocrats	*Mather Winthrop Hancock p. 41*	*Roosevelt Van Renssalaer p. 41*	*Byrd Pinckney p. 41*	
Local Government	*township p. 46*	*variety*	*county/parish p. 47*	
Facts of Interest	*coldest climate p. 36*		*first blacks p. 42*	*the Wilderness Road*

bread colonies
fishing/whaling
fur trade
plantations
shipbuilding

hilly
navigable rivers
rich, thick soil
thin, rocky soil
tidewater
wide coastal plain

Boston
Charleston
Jamestown
Nantucket
New Bedford
Philadelphia
Savannah

melting pot
mostly English
mostly English

Byrd
Hancock
Mather
Pinckney
Roosevelt
Van Renssalaer
Winthrop

county/parish
township

coldest climate
first blacks

American Republic

Chapter 3   Activity C

The Busy Life of Josiah Hancock

Use these words to complete the story about a fictional character named Josiah Hancock.

aristocrats	justices of the peace	redemptioners
Boston	militia	royal colonies
bread colonies	Nantucket	subsistence farmers
freeholders	plantations	tidewater
indentured servants	power of the purse	township

Josiah Hancock is a popular leader among the upper class, or (1) __aristocrats   p. 40__ .

He is a busy merchant whose office is located in the port of (2) __Boston   p. 35 (map)__ in

Massachusetts Bay. He has little interaction with New England's (3) __subsistence farmers   p. 36__ ,

who barely make enough to feed and clothe their own families. Instead, he trades with the

wealthy farmers who live in Pennsylvania, one of the (4) __bread colonies   p. 37__ , which

are famous for their rich soil. Hancock also trades with aristocrats in South Carolina, whose

large farms are called (5) __plantations   p. 38__ . Their main money crop is rice, grown

along the coastal rivers and inlets (the (6) __tidewater   p. 38__). They trade rice for

whale oil, processed at (7) __Nantucket   p. 36__ .

Hancock provides free passage to young Englishmen who agree to work in his office seven

years as (8) __indentured servants   p. 41__ . Sometimes he hires (9) __redemptioners   p. 41__ from

Europe, who bring their families and work in his home for two years. As an aristocrat, Hancock

takes his duties seriously. He has been appointed the commander of the local army, or

(10) __militia   p. 45__ . Because he is one of the town's (11) __freeholders   p. 46__

(property owners), Hancock can vote and hold office in the basic unit of government, called a

(12) __township   p. 46__ . After the colony came under the king's control in 1686 as

one of the (13) __royal colonies   p. 44__ , the legislature has attempted to limit the gover-

nor through the (14) __power of the purse   p. 45__ . Hancock is especially concerned that the

governor appoint honest (15) __justices of the peace   p. 45__ , who collect taxes and try those ac-

cused of crimes.

American Republic

Chapter 3   Activity D

Colonial Society

Underline the word or phrase that best completes each sentence.

1. Nine out of ten early colonists were (merchants, <u>farmers</u>). *p. 36*

2. A farmer who raises just enough crops and livestock to feed his family is called a (<u>subsistence</u>, tidewater) farmer. *p. 36*

3. New England's climate was (warmer, <u>colder</u>) than the climates of other colonial regions. *p. 36*

4. The Grand Banks off the coast of Newfoundland became famous for its large schools of (<u>codfish</u>, salmon). *p. 36*

5. Almost all the settlers in (<u>Massachusetts</u>, Pennsylvania) were British. *p. 37*

6. Important trade centers arose near New England's (<u>harbors</u>, frontier). *p. 37*

7. A colony influenced by diverse peoples is called a (<u>melting pot</u>, salad bowl). *p. 37*

8. The middle colonies grew an abundance of (<u>cereal grains</u>, indigo). *p. 37*

9. A major advantage of the middle colonies was their (tidewater areas, <u>navigable rivers</u>). *p. 37*

10. An early center for fur trade was (New Bedford, <u>Albany</u>). *p. 38*

11. The foothills of the (<u>Appalachian</u>, Blue Ridge) Mountains are called the Piedmont. *p. 38*

12. Coopers used lumber to make barrels, and wainwrights used it to make (boats, <u>wagons</u>). *p. 38*

13. Britain's large estates became the pattern for the (<u>plantations</u>, townships) in the southern colonies. *p. 38*

14. The first important money crop in the southern colonies was (<u>tobacco</u>, indigo). *p. 38*

15. The largest and most important crop in all the colonies was (<u>corn</u>, rice). *p. 38*

16. A popular term for the colonial frontier was the (trenches, <u>back country</u>). *p. 39*

17. The most land that a frontier settler could clear was about (<u>two hundred</u>, two thousand) acres. *pp. 39-40*

18. Frontier settlers usually ate their food on wooden (<u>trenchers</u>, noggins). *p. 40*

19. The main north-south colonial highway was the (<u>Great Wagon</u>, Wilderness) Road. *p. 40*

20. The members of the upper class were called (freeholders, <u>aristocrats</u>). *p. 40*

21. The possessions of the colonial aristocrats were usually made in (<u>Europe</u>, New England). *p. 41*

22. European families who hoped a relative would help them pay the cost of passage to America when they arrived were called (<u>redemptioners</u>, indentured servants). *p. 41*

23. Most masters wanted their indentured servants to be (<u>single</u>, married). *p. 41*

24. The first blacks in America came to (Charleston, <u>Jamestown</u>). *p. 42*

25. The most expensive worker was the (indentured servant, <u>slave</u>). *p. 42*

26. Black slaves in New England usually served in the (<u>homes</u>, fields). *p. 43*

27. Both slaves and free workers labored (eight, <u>fourteen</u>) hours a day. *p. 43*

28. In (<u>charter</u>, proprietary) colonies the people elected their own governor and legislature. *p. 44*

29. One method that colonial legislatures used to limit the royal governor's power was the (<u>power of the purse</u>, justice of the peace). *p. 45*

30. The main source of income for the colonial governments was (<u>property</u>, income) taxes. *p. 45*

31. The basic unit of government in New England was the (parish, <u>township</u>). *p. 46*

32. The town meeting was America's purest form of (<u>direct</u>, representative) government. *p. 46*

33. "Putting out" was a common form of (<u>poor relief</u>, punishment) in New England. *p. 47*

American Republic

Case #1: The Northeast in Peril

The Geographic Intelligence Agency (GIA) has uncovered a plot by Captain Barney Kull and his crustaceous crew to take over the northeastern United States. The criminals are planning to contaminate water supplies across the region with high dosages of cod-liver oil. If the criminals succeed, the whole Northeast may become as crusty and ornery as they are. The GIA has managed to place an undercover lobster on Captain Barney's ship, the *Crabby Queen*. He's been able to overhear the location for the cod-liver oil drop points, but the information is vague. The GIA has called on master sleuth Sir Henry Vey to decipher the clues. Use the maps and text from the first three chapters and the map of the Northeast (page 51) to help Sir Vey save the region from certain crustiness.

Drop point #1: The city that was called New Amsterdam when the Dutch controlled the colony

___New York___ p. 25 (map)___

Drop point #2: The state capital located in the Green Mountains ___Montpelier___ p. 51___

Drop point #3: The home of the nation's steel industry ___Pittsburgh___ p. 50___

Drop point #4: The city bearing the name of George and Cecilius Calvert's official title

___Baltimore___ p. 30___

Drop point #5: The city known as Fort Christina when the Swedes controlled the colony

___Wilmington___ p. 27___

Drop point #6: The bay on which Jamestown was founded ___Chesapeake Bay___ p. 10___

Drop point #7: The state capital found on the Delmarva Peninsula ___Dover___ p. 51___

Drop point #8: The lake that Burlington is located on ___Lake Champlain___ _p. 51_____

Drop point #9: The state capital located closest to the line of longitude seventy degrees west

_____Augusta___ _p. 51_____

Drop point #10: The city founded by Thomas Hooker in 1636 ___Hartford___ _p. 23_____

Drop point #11: The river found by Jacques Cartier that gave the French claim to much of North

America ___St. Lawrence River___ _p. 9_____

Drop point #12: The mountains north of the Mohawk River ___Adirondack Mountains___ _p. 51____

Drop point #13: The major city in New York located on Lake Erie ___Buffalo___ _p. 51_____

Drop point #14: The city known as Fort Orange when the Dutch controlled the colony

_____Albany___ _p. 26 (map)_____

Drop point #15: The town settled by Puritans in 1628 in present-day Massachusetts

_____Salem___ _p. 17 (chart)_____

Drop point #16: The bay in which the Mayflower Compact was signed ___Cape Cod Bay___ _p. 51___

Drop point #17: The major mountain peak about seventy-five miles north of Concord

_____Mt. Washington___ _p. 51_____

Drop point #18: The capital of the state where the Pine Barrens are found ___Trenton___ _p. 51_____

Drop point #19: The mountains where the Connecticut River begins ___White Mountains___ _p. 51___

Drop point #20: Colonial town located just north of Hartford ___Windsor___ _p. 24 (map)_____

American Republic

Chapter 4   Activity A

Simple Outlining

Look at the headings for Chapter 4 and then complete the outline.

A. Religious Backgrounds of the Colonies

    1. Puritan New England

    2. _The Southern Colonies   p. 53_____

    3. _The Middle Colonies   p. 55_____

B. The Great Awakening

    1. _Leaders of the Great Awakening   p. 58_____

    2. _Effects of the Great Awakening   p. 59_____

    3. Opponents of the Great Awakening

        a. Deism

        b. _Unitarianism   p. 62_____

C. _Colonial Education   p. 63_____

    1. _Grammar Schools   p. 63_____

        a. _Schools in New England   p. 64_____

        b. _Schools in the Middle and Southern Colonies   p. 64___

    2. _Higher Education   p. 65_____

    3. _Vocational "Schools"   p. 66_____

D. _Colonial Arts and Crafts   p. 66_____

    1. _Glassware   p. 66_____

    2. _Metalworking   p. 66_____

    3. _Clocks   p. 67_____

    4. _Furniture   p. 68_____

    5. _Architecture   p. 69_____

    6. _Painting   p. 70_____

American Republic

Scripture in Colonial Society

Scripture had a major impact on the colonies. Almost everyone could quote it, and most people accepted its morals. But knowledge of the Bible does not save people or keep them from error. During the Great Awakening the Holy Spirit awakened many Americans from their spiritual sleep, while others remained in their sins. Use your Bible to answer these questions.

1. One influence of Christianity in America was "the Protestant work ethic." Believing that labor had spiritual value, the Puritans emphasized honest, hard work. Americans have been industrious ever since.

   • What type of labor is profitable (Prov. 14:23)? ___all labor___

   • How hard does God expect us to work (Eccles. 9:10)? ___with all our might___

   • What is one purpose of our work (Eph. 4:28)? ___to give to others___

2. Benjamin Franklin was a leader in the Enlightenment. He believed in hard work and accepted Jesus' "system of morals," but he rejected the Savior. He believed that our "most acceptable service of God was the doing of good to man."

   • Whose help do we need to accomplish good (John 15:4-5)? ___Jesus Christ's___

   • What does Jesus call the work of those He never knew (Matt. 7:22-23)? ___iniquity___

   • What is the most important commandment (Mark 12:30)? ___Love God.___

3. Franklin trusted his own reasoning above Scripture. Raised a Presbyterian, he rejected the church's teachings because they were "unintelligible" or "doubtful." He even boasted that George Whitefield used "sometimes to pray for my conversion, but never had the satisfaction of believing that his prayers were heard."

   • How well can an unbeliever understand spiritual truths (I Cor. 2:14)? ___He cannot.___

   • How does God's intelligence compare to man's (Isa. 55:8-9)? ___infinite___

   • How trustworthy is our own heart (Jer. 17:9)? ___It is deceitful.___

   • Who should people trust above their own understanding (Prov. 3:5-6)? ___the Lord___

   • Where does knowledge start (Prov. 1:7)? ___with the fear of the Lord___

4. Many churchgoers attacked the Great Awakening because of its emotional displays, so Jonathan Edwards wrote a book to defend the revival as a great work of God.

   • Why do some churchgoers despise good preaching (II Tim. 4:2-3)? ___selfish desires___

   • What does God call the worship by unbelievers (Isa. 1:13-16)? ___iniquity; evil___

   • What is one biblical response to warnings of judgment (Hab. 3:16)? ___trembling___

   • What is the main evidence of true conversion (II Cor. 5:17)? ___a new way of life___

   • What is a key ingredient of true revival (II Chron. 7:14)? ___repentance___

American Republic

Chapter 4   Activity C

David Brainerd's *Diary* and *Journal*

Brainerd's works were published by his father-in-law, Jonathan Edwards. The diary entry describes one of his first Sundays among the Indians. The other entry, written in a journal he kept for his sponsoring missionary society, describes a day near the end of his brief ministry.

from Brainerd's *Diary*

Lord's Day, July 1 [1744]. In the morning, was perplexed with wandering vain thoughts; was much grieved, judged and condemned myself before God. And oh, how miserable did I feel because I could not live to God! At ten, rode away with a heavy heart, to preach to my Indians. . . . In the afternoon, I felt still barren when I began to preach, and after about half an hour I seemed to myself to know nothing and to have nothing to say to the Indians; but soon after, I found in myself a spirit of love, and warmth, and power, to address the poor Indians. God helped me to plead with them. . . . When I came away from them, I spent the whole time, while I was riding to my lodgings three miles distant, in prayer and praise to God.

After I rode more than two miles, it came into my mind to dedicate myself to God again. . . . My heart rejoiced in my particular work as a missionary; rejoiced in my necessity of self-denial in many respects. I still continued to give up myself to God and implore mercy of Him, praying incessantly, every moment, with sweet fervency. My nature being very weak of late, and much spent, was now considerably overcome. My fingers grew very feeble and somewhat numb, so that I could scarcely stretch them out straight. When I lighted from my horse I could hardly walk, my joints seemed all to be loosed. But I felt abundant strength in the inner man.

from Brainerd's *Journal*

March 24 [1746]. Numbered the Indians to see how many souls God had gathered together here since my coming into these parts, and found there were now about an hundred and thirty persons together, old and young. Sundry of these that are my stated hearers, perhaps to the number of fifteen or twenty, were absent at this season. . . .

My people went out this day upon the design of clearing some of their land, above fifteen miles from this settlement, in order to their settling there in a compact form; where they might be under advantages of attending the public worship of God, of having their children taught in a school; and at the same time have a conveniency for planting, their land in the place of our present residence being of little or no value for that purpose. The design of their settling thus in a body, and cultivating their lands (which they have done very little in their pagan state), being of such necessity and importance, . . . I thought it proper to call them together, and show them the duty of laboring with faithfulness and industry; and that they must not now "be slothful in business" as they had ever been in their pagan state.

1. What did Brainerd mean by "my Indians"? *The lost Indians were his personal mission field.*

2. Name two personal difficulties that Brainerd faced in his ministry. *depression, illness*

3. How did Brainerd travel? *horseback*

4. About how many Indians did God save after Brainerd's arrival? *about 145 to 150*

5. What cultural changes accompanied the Indians' conversion? *towns, churches, farms, schools*

American Republic

Chapter 4   Activity D

New England Primer

The *New England Primer,* published in the 1680s, was the first and most popular school reader in the American colonies. Three million copies were sold over a span of almost two hundred years. Each letter of the alphabet was accompanied by two rhyming lines. Try to complete each rhyme. What two letters were missing in the alphabet? *(i, v)*

In Adam's fall

We sinned all.

Thy life to mend

This Book attend.

The Cat doth play

And after slay.

A Dog will bite

A thief at ___night___ .

An Eagle's flight

Is out of ___sight___ .

The idle fool

Is whipped at ___school___ .

As runs the [hour] Glass,

Our life doth ___pass___ .

My book and Heart

Shall never ___part___ .

Job feels the rod

Yet blesses ___God___ .

Our King the good

No man of blood.

The Lion bold

The Lamb doth ___hold___ .

The moon gives ___light___

In time of night.

Nightingales ___sing___

In time of spring.

The royal Oak was the tree

That saved his royal majesty.

___Peter___ denies

His Lord and cries.

Queen Esther comes in

  royal state

To save the Jews from

  dismal fate.

Rachel doth mourn

For her first ___born___ .

Samuel anoints

Whom God ___appoints___ .

Time cuts down all

Both great and ___small___ .

Uriah's beauteous wife

Made David seek his life.

Whales in the sea

God's voice obey.

Xerxes the Great did die

And so must you & ___I___ .

Youth's forward slips

Death soonest nips.

___Zacchaeus___ he

did climb the tree

His Lord to see.

American Republic

Clues to America's Past in Your Home

Almost every home has some interesting arts and crafts, including designs from the colonial era. Of special interest to historians are heirlooms (valued possessions passed down through the family for generations). With the help of an adult in your family, complete this survey.

1. Who is your family's earliest known ancestor that grew up in America? Try to find these facts about him or her.

   name _____   location _____

   denomination _____   occupation _____

   education (apprenticeship, dame, grammar, college) _____

2. What heirlooms are in your home? Check every type of heirloom that has been passed down at least three generations (from your grandparents or earlier). Give one example of each and circle the oldest.

   ❏ glassware _____   ❏ jewelry _____

   ❏ silverware/pewter _____   ❏ quilts/samplers _____

   ❏ clocks _____   ❏ furniture _____

   ❏ weapons _____   ❏ paintings/portraits _____

   ❏ tools _____   ❏ books _____

   ❏ family records _____   ❏ other _____

3. What crafts in your home imitate old styles? Check every type of craft that your family has made or purchased. Circle any craft that you have made.

   ❏ oil lamps/candles _____   ❏ embroidery/samplers _____

   ❏ clocks _____   ❏ furniture _____

   ❏ rugs/quilts _____   ❏ baskets _____

   ❏ tools _____   ❏ other _____

4. Many homes in America continue to imitate old architectural styles. If your own home or one in your area has any of these features, give the location in the blank.

   ❏ log home _____   ❏ Georgian architecture _____

   ❏ loft _____   ❏ clapboard siding _____

   ❏ cornices _____   ❏ lean-to _____

American Republic

Chapter 4   Activity F

Who Am I?

Read each statement and decide who would have said it. Write your answer in the blank.

David Zeisberger
p. 56

1. The Delaware Indians suffered many wrongs before God blessed us in the "Golden Age of Indian Work."

William Tennent
p. 58

2. The graduates of my "log college" became God's instruments to spread revival throughout the middle colonies.

Samuel Davies
p. 58

3. God used me to help spread the Great Awakening to Virginia and the other southern colonies.

Jonathan Edwards
p. 58

4. My congregation in Massachusetts experienced revival when I preached "Sinners in the Hands of an Angry God."

George Whitefield
p. 59

5. I thank the Lord for the wonderful revivals that occurred during my seven evangelistic trips to the American colonies.

David Brainerd
p. 60

6. I refused to let my youth and the pain of my tuberculosis keep me from giving the gospel to the Indians.

Noah Webster
p. 63

7. My *Blue-Backed Speller*, published in 1783, became the model for spelling in the colonies.

Seth Thomas
pp. 67-68

8. I founded a clock-making company in Connecticut that still exists today.

Duncan Phyfe
p. 69

9. To make high-quality furniture, I paid up to $1,000 for a single log of mahogany.

John Singleton Copley
pp. 70-71

10. I never dreamed that I would one day have a reputation as "the greatest painter ever to work in colonial America."

What Am I?

Read each statement and decide what it describes. Write the correct answer in the blank.

Congregationalists
p. 53

11. This denomination sprang from New England Puritans, whose churches were controlled by the congregation, not a bishop.

Halfway Covenant
p. 53

12. This unfortunate compromise in 1662 allowed the unsaved children of Puritans to become church members.

Church of England
p. 53

13. This was the official denomination in all southern colonies.

Moravians
pp. 54-55

14. This denomination, formed by followers of John Huss, believed in winning the Indians through missions.

Jews
p. 55

15. This religious group was denied the right to worship freely in the colonies because it was considered pagan.

Enlightenment
p. 62

16. This eighteenth-century movement exalted man's ability to think above God's revealed truth.

deism
p. 62

17. This philosophy asserted that God was a Watchmaker who established unchangeable laws of nature.

grammar school
p. 63

18. Parents sent their children here to learn math, natural philosophy, Latin, and Greek.

Harvard College
p. 65

19. Founded to train Puritan ministers, this was the first chartered institution of higher learning in the colonies.

pewter
p. 66

20. This alloy of tin, lead, and copper (known as "poor man's silver") was used to make plates and bowls in the colonies.

Skill: Recognition

American Republic

Chapter 5   Activity A

Map Study: The French and Indian War

Refer to the map in the textbook on page 79 to complete the map below.

1. Label these rivers:
St. Lawrence
Mississippi
Allegheny
Monongahela

2. Label these cities and forts:
Quebec
Montreal
Albany
Fort Duquesne
Boston
Philadelphia
New Orleans

3. Using a colored pencil, color the region that France lost to Britain in the Peace of Paris (1763).

4. Using another colored pencil, color the region that Spain lost to Britain in the Peace of Paris.

5. Draw these figures at the places where these events occurred:

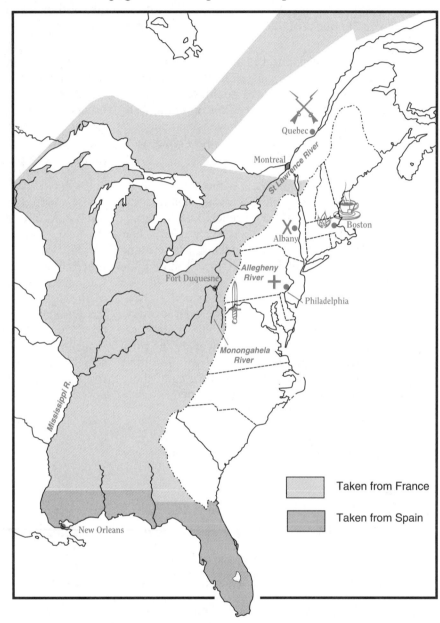

Taken from France

Taken from Spain

 Braddock's defeat *p. 77*

 Wolfe's victory *p. 78*

 the "Tea Party" *p. 86*

 first fighting of the Revolutionary War *p. 89*

 Franklin's unsuccessful Plan of Union *p. 76*

 the successful First Continental Congress *p. 88*

American Republic

Chapter 5   Activity B

George Washington's Report on the Defeat of Braddock

Edward Braddock's defeat near Fort Duquesne had a major influence on colonial opinion of British troops. Read Washington's letter to his mother, dated July 18, 1755. Then answer the questions.

Honored Madam: As I doubt not but you have heard of our defeat, and, perhaps, had it represented in a worse light, if possible, than it deserves, I have taken this earliest opportunity to give you some account of the engagement as it happened, within ten miles of the French fort, on Wednesday, the 9th instant.

We marched to that place, without any considerable loss, having only now and then a straggler picked up by the French and scouting Indians. When we came there, we were attacked by a party of French and Indians, whose number, I am persuaded, did not exceed three hundred men; while ours consisted of about one thousand three hundred well-armed troops, chiefly regular soldiers, who were struck with such panic that they behaved with more cowardice than it is possible to conceive. The officers behaved gallantly, in order to encourage their men, for which they suffered greatly, there being near sixty killed and wounded; a large proportion of the number we had.

The Virginia troops showed a good deal of bravery, and were nearly all killed; for I believe, out of three companies that were there, scarcely thirty men were left alive. . . . The dastardly behavior of those they call regulars exposed all others, that were inclined to do their duty, to almost certain death; and, at last, in despite of all the efforts of the officers to the contrary, they ran, as sheep pursued by dogs, and it was impossible to rally them.

The General was wounded, of which he died three days after. Sir Peter Halket was killed in the field, where died many other brave officers. I luckily escaped without a wound, though I had four bullets through my coat, and two horses shot under me. Captains Orme and Morris, two of the aides-de-camp, were wounded early in the engagement, which rendered the duty harder upon me, as I was the only person then left to distribute the General's orders, which I was scarcely able to do, as I was not half recovered from a violent illness, that had confined me to my bed and a wagon for above ten days. . . .

I am, honored Madam, your most dutiful son.

1. Whom did Washington blame for the defeat? _British regulars_

2. Which troops performed well? _Virginia troops (from Washington's home colony)_

3. What evidence do you see of Washington's bravery? _four bullet holes; two dead horses_

4. What factors limited Washington's performance as an aide? _scarcity of aides; illness_

5. The French had about nine hundred men at the battle. Why do you think Washington underestimated their numbers? How does his mistake affect our opinion of the British?

   Washington's view was restricted by the woods, and he was writing immediately

   after the event. The British appeared to be incompetent cowards. (But they

   lasted two hours against a large, hidden foe.)

6. Why doesn't Washington give an opinion of Braddock? _Braddock did a poor job, so_

   Washington probably wanted to show respect for the dead.

American Republic

Chapter 5   Activity C

Preparedness for War

Complete the chart by describing the advantages and disadvantages of each side at the start of the French and Indian War. Underline the facts that are an *advantage*.

	French p. 75	**British** p. 75
Unity of Government	*strong and unified*	*no central colonial organization; little cooperation*
Defenses/Forts	*strategic forts along inland waterways*	*predominance of coastal cities*
Army Training	*well trained*	*inexperienced regular army and colonials*
Support of Indians	*many Indian tribes*	*Iroquois confederation*
Population	*sparse*	*fifteen times the size of New France*
Size of Region to Defend	*widely scattered settlements*	*compact on the Atlantic coast*
Navy	*moderate size*	*largest in the world*

Steps to Independence

Underline the word or phrase that best completes each sentence.

1. The Albany Plan of Union was a (success, <u>failure</u>). p. 76
2. The Peace of Paris (1763) gave Britain control of all lands (<u>east</u>, west) of the Mississippi. p. 78
3. After the Seven Years' War, Britain (<u>increased</u>, decreased) control of her colonies. p. 78
4. A popular colonial protest was "No taxation without (authorization, <u>representation</u>)!" p. 82
5. The colonial boycotts (helped, <u>hurt</u>) British merchants. p. 82
6. When the king rejected its petition, the Stamp Act Congress advocated (war, <u>boycotts</u>). p. 82
7. The Sons of Liberty were organized to protest the (<u>Stamp Act</u>, Tea Act). p. 82
8. Boston's Committee of Correspondence was headed by (<u>Samuel Adams</u>, Patrick Henry). p. 85
9. The Tea Act caused the price of British tea to (increase, <u>decrease</u>). p. 86
10. The Quebec Act (<u>followed</u>, preceded) the Boston Tea Party. p. 86
11. The Boston Tea Party caused Britain to pass the (Townshend, <u>Intolerable</u>) Acts. p. 86
12. The First Continental Congress sought to (overthrow, <u>petition</u>) the king. p. 89
13. Colonial protests caused Britain to (repeal, <u>reinforce</u>) the Intolerable Acts. p. 89
14. The first shots of the War for Independence were fired at (<u>Lexington</u>, Concord). p. 89
15. In their first fight, the "redcoats" suffered (<u>more</u>, fewer) casualties than the minutemen. p. 90

American Republic

Chapter 5   Activity D

Words You Need to Know: Causes and Effects

Although the American Revolution surprised most people, in hindsight it seems the natural outgrowth of a long series of events. One group's actions led to another group's reactions. Historians want to know the causes (*why* these actions took place) and the effects (*what* the results were). Complete the chart by writing down the causes of the British actions and the effects, or colonial reactions. The answers are listed at the bottom.

Cause	British Action	Colonial Reaction
lack of colonial unity	failure in the French and Indian War (1754)	*Albany Plan of Union*
William Pitt's system	Peace of Paris (1763)	*desire for no more British troops*
Pontiac's revolt p. 80	Proclamation of 1763	*anger over closed lands*
costly British troops in America p. 80	Quartering Act of 1765	*anger over troops in homes*
British need for more money pp. 81-82	Stamp Act of 1765	*Stamp Act Congress*
strong leadership in Parliament after the repeal of the Stamp Act	Townshend Acts (1767)	*new boycotts and smuggling p. 83*
British troops stationed in Boston pp. 83-84	Boston Massacre (1770)	*radical accounts of "martyrs"*
difficulties of the British East India Company pp. 85-86	Tea Act of 1773	*Boston Tea Party*
British anger at the failure of Massachusetts to obey the Tea Act	Intolerable Acts (1774)	*First Continental Congress p. 88*
Declaration of Rights and Grievances pp. 88-89	George III now says: "Submit or triumph."	*stockpiling of colonial arms*
British attempt to capture colonial arms pp. 89-90	Battles of Lexington and Concord (1775)	*start of the War for Independence*

Causes
British attempt to capture colonial arms
British need for more money
British troops stationed in Boston
costly British troops in America
Declaration of Rights and Grievances
difficulties of the British East India Company
Pontiac's revolt

Colonial Reactions
anger over closed lands
anger over troops in homes
Boston Tea Party
First Continental Congress
new boycotts and smuggling
Stamp Act Congress
start of the War for Independence
stockpiling of colonial arms

Skills: Vocabulary/Cause and Effect

American Republic

Chapter 5   Activity E

Writing Your Own Glossary

A *glossary* is "a list of important terms with their definitions." Write a short description of each term below. Your description should include the words in the right column.

Example:
France

Britain's *greatest* rival *during the eighteenth century*

rival, Britain

People

1. Iroquois
   p. 75

   strongest Indian confederation *in America;* became a major British ally

   confederation, British ally

2. George Washington
   pp. 76-77

   military leader from Virginia who lost *Fort* Necessity *and later became a British* aide

   Virginia, lost, aide

3. Edward Braddock
   p. 77

   British general *who* lost *a battle at Fort* Duquesne *and died as a result of a wound*

   British general, lost, died

4. William Pitt
   p. 77

   British leader *whose* new system *helped* Britain win the French and Indian War

   British leader, new system

5. James Wolfe
   p. 78

   British general *who won a major battle at* Quebec but was mortally wounded

   British general, won

6. Pontiac
   p. 80

   Ottawa chief *who organized many* Indian tribes on the frontier

   Ottawa chief, frontier

7. Samuel Adams
   p. 82

   leader from Massachusetts who led the opposition *against Britain*

   Massachusetts, opposition

8. Patrick Henry
   p. 87

   leader from Virginia *who gave the famous* speech, "Give me liberty *or give me death!"*

   Virginia, speech, liberty

Terms

9. mercantilism
   p. 81

   European economic system *that measured* wealth by the gold *a nation possessed*

   economic system, gold

10. writs of assistance   *p. 81*

    general search warrants *that the* British used to search for smuggled goods

    search warrants, British

11. duties   *p. 81*

    taxes *on* imported goods

    imported goods, taxes

12. Committees of Correspondence
    p. 85

    committees that promoted opposition *to Bri-*tain *and* alerted *the colonies of British threats*

    opposition, alerted

Places

13. Ohio Valley
p. 76
region where a struggle for control helped _cause the French and Indian War_ — struggle, war

14. Fort Duquesne
pp. 76-77
original name of Fort Pitt (modern Pittsburgh) at the start of the Ohio River — Fort Pitt, Ohio

15. Quebec
pp. 77-78
key city in New France whose defeat brought an end to the French and Indian War — New France, defeat

16. Lexington and Concord *pp. 89-90*
site of British skirmishes over colonial stockpiles that marked the beginning of war — skirmishes, beginning

Events

17. French and Indian War *p. 76*
name of the Seven Years' War in America — Seven Years' War, America

18. Albany Plan
p. 76
Franklin's attempt to unite the colonies during the French and Indian War — unite, colonies

19. Proclamation of 1763 *p. 80*
British law that forbade colonial settlement west of the Appalachian Mountains — forbade, west, Appalachian

20. Navigation and Trade Acts *p. 81*
Britain's policies that regulated colonial trade with Britain's competitors — colonial trade, regulated

21. Sugar Act
p. 81
British attempt to get money from the colonies through duties — British, money, duties

22. Stamp Act
pp. 81-82
British attempt to increase revenue through stamps required on business documents — British, stamps, revenue

23. Townshend Acts
p. 83
renewed duties on colonial goods, which caused resentment to mount in the colonies — renewed duties, resentment

24. Boston Massacre
pp. 83-84
the death of five "martyrs" who were shot while taunting British soldiers — death, five, "martyrs"

25. Boston Tea Party
pp. 85-86
colonial protest of the Tea Act by tossing over the tea on tea ships in port at Boston — tea ships, protest

26. Intolerable Acts
p. 86
British attempt to punish Massachusetts by closing the port of Boston and taking away freedoms — Massachusetts, punish

27. Quebec Act
p. 86
British act that gave favored status to French law and Roman Catholicism — favored, French, Catholicism

American Republic

Chapter 6   Activity A

Map Study: The War for Independence

Refer to the maps in the textbook on pages 97, 100, and 108 to complete the map below.

1. Label these bodies of water: Lake Champlain, Hudson River, Delaware River.

2. Label these locations (black dots): Valley Forge, Albany, West Point, Boston.

3. Label these battle sites (red dots for British victories and blue for colonial victories): Bunker Hill, Montreal, Quebec, Saratoga, Harlem Heights, Monmouth, Trenton, Brandywine, Yorktown, Guilford Courthouse, Kings Mountain, Cowpens, Camden, Charleston, Savannah.

Students will see the sequence of events in the three regions, not troop movements.

4. Using a colored pencil, draw a line to connect the battle sites of the northern campaigns (1775-76) in the order the events occurred. (Hint: Begin with Bunker Hill and end with the evacuation of Boston.) Using another color, connect the sites in the middle campaigns (1776-78). Using a third color, connect the sites in the southern campaigns (1779-81). Draw an arrow at the end of each line.

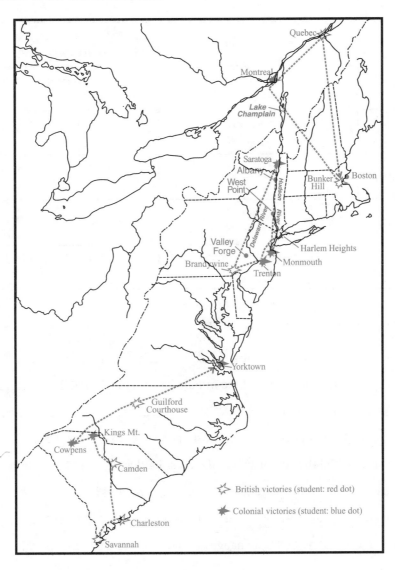

American Republic

Chapter 6   Activity B

Major Battles

Complete the chart. For each battle, include the commanders of each side if they are mentioned in the text. Also place an asterisk (*) beside each battle that the colonists won.

	Battle	Year	Leaders	Significance
Northern Campaigns	*Fort Ticonderoga p. 96	1775	Ethan Allen Benedict Arnold	capture of artillery used to later free Boston
	Bunker Hill pp. 96-97	1775	William Prescott William Howe	patriots' failure to capture Boston; heavy British casualties
	Quebec pp. 97-98	1775	Richard Montgomery Benedict Arnold	last patriot attack on Canada; colonial respect for the British army
Middle Campaigns	Long Island p. 100	1776	George Washington William Howe	British capture of New York; miraculous escape of the Continental Army
	*Trenton p. 101	1776	George Washington	patriots' capture of a Hessian outpost; improvement of colonial morale
	*Saratoga p. 103	1777	Horatio Gates John Burgoyne	surrender of a British army; France's official entry into the war
Southern Campaigns	*Vincennes p. 104	1779	George Rogers Clark "Hair Buyer" Hamilton	colonial claim to the frontier
	*Kings Mountain p. 107	1780	Patrick Ferguson	over-mountain men's defeat of a large Tory force
	*Cowpens pp. 106-7	1781	Daniel Morgan Banastre Tarleton	patriot defeat of a British force
	*Yorktown p. 108	1781	George Washington Charles Cornwallis	surrender of a British army; British desire for peace

Answer these questions based on the chart.

1. What was the colonists' first defeat? __Bunker Hill__

2. What was the last major battle of the middle campaigns? __Saratoga__

3. Which year includes the most battles? __1775__

4. Which colonial commander won the most battles? __George Washington__

5. In which region did the colonists win the most battles? __southern campaigns__

6. Which battle did *not* take place in the three major regions? __Vincennes__

7. Which battle do you think was the *least* important? __Answers will vary.__

8. What battle caused the greatest changes in the war? __Answers will vary.__

American Republic

Chapter 6   Activity C

Crossword Puzzle

Across

2. American naval officer (initials)   *p. 105*
5. another term for a Tory   *p. 99*
8. term for supporters of independence   *p. 99*
10. colonial victory after Trenton   *p. 101*
pp. 103-4 12. British commander at Monmouth
p. 99 14. Declaration of _____ (July 4, 1776)
15. American negotiator in Paris   *p. 108*
p. 108 16. America's western boundary in 1783
p. 98 19. city overlooked by Dorchester Heights
20. term for a hired soldier   *p. 97*
23. merchant vessel outfitted to fight   *p. 105*
p. 102 24. patriotic spy who died for his country
25. "Mad _____" Bailey   *p. 106*
p. 104 27. captured the Ohio Valley with few men
28. de Grasse's surprise   *pp. 107-8*
29. Thomas Paine's *Common* _____   *p. 98*

Down

1. the Continental Congress that declared war   *p. 96*
2. author of the Declaration of Independence   *p. 99*
3. young French officer   *p. 107*
4. New Hampshire's Green Mountain _____   *p. 96*
6. colony where Cornwallis was trapped   *p. 108*
7. Prussian drill master   *p. 103*
9. type of branch that symbolizes peace   *p. 96*
11. "over-_____ men" of the Piedmont   *p. 107*
13. official title of the patriot army   *p. 96*
17. serious grievance of Pennsylvanian troops   *p. 103*
18. Washington's bad winter at Valley _____   *p. 103*
21. meeting place in Britain's 1777 attack plan   *p. 101*
22. location of peace talks   *p. 108*
23. pamphleteer   *p. 98*
26. patriot quartermaster (initials)   *p. 103*

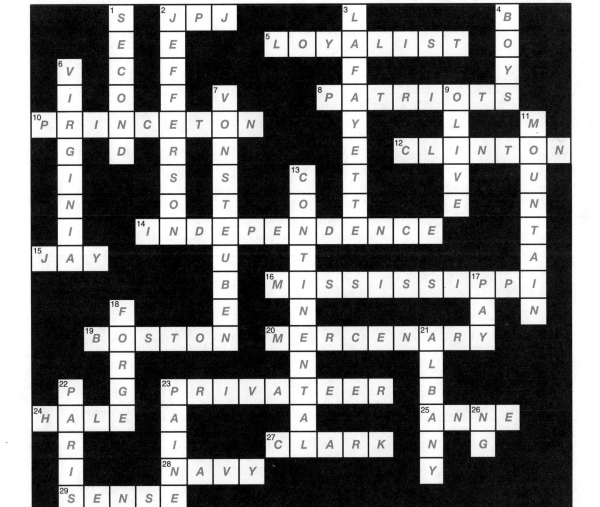

American Republic

Chapter 7   Activity A

Need for the Constitution ☆ *Classroom discussion*

Although Americans feared strong government, they discovered that weakness is just as bad. At the Constitutional Convention the states accepted some solutions immediately, but others required compromise. For each weakness below, give one harmful result and the solution. If the solution was a compromise, describe the nature of the compromise; otherwise, write "none."

Weakness Under Confederation	Harmful Results	Solution Under Constitution	Nature of the Compromise
states' power to coin money	*worthless money; inability of farmers to pay debts; Shays's Rebellion*	*power to coin money reserved to Congress*	*none*
no executive branch pp. 118-19, 125-26	*no power to enforce laws; no army to take British forts; no power against pirates; no leader to force Spain to grant the right of deposit*	*presidency*	*none*
no judicial branch pp. 118, 125-26	*no power to interpret the laws; no power to enforce the laws*	*judicial branch*	*none*
no power to tax pp. 118-19, 127	*lack of funds to run government; inability to pay debts to soldiers, bondholders, and foreign nations (France and the Netherlands)*	*power to tax*	*none*
no power to regulate trade pp. 118-19, 127	*disputes over taxing imports; disputes over navigation rights*	*Commerce Compromise*	*navigation laws passed by simple majority vote; no state taxes on imports*
equal votes for each state pp. 125-27	*difficulty of passing laws; unequal representation*	*Great (Connecticut) Compromise*	*New Jersey (Small State) Plan in the Senate; Virginia (Large State) Plan in the House*
tax assessments ignored slaves p. 127	*dispute over counting slaves for taxes and representation*	*three-fifths compromise*	*slaves counted as three-fifths of a person for taxes and representation*

American Republic

What God Says About Government

The framers of the Constitution were familiar with scriptural principles of government. In fact, the Father of the Constitution, James Madison, spent three years studying under Rev. John Witherspoon, the president of Princeton. Use your Bible to answer these questions about the nature of man, the role of government, and God's role in government.

1. Madison acknowledged man's sinful nature. In *The Federalist* he wrote, "If men were angels, no government would be necessary. . . . In framing a government which is to be administered by men over men, the great difficulty lies in this: you must first enable the government to control the governed; and in the next place oblige it to control itself."

   • How many people have sinful desires (Rom. 3:10-12)? ___*everyone*___

   • Name two crimes that people enjoy (Rom. 1:28-32). ___*murder, breaking agreements, etc.*___

   • What happens when men are free from government (Gen. 6:5, 11)? ___*violence/evil*___

   • What is a major temptation for rulers (I Sam. 8:10-18)? ___*abuse of power*___

   • How do rulers and their subjects respond to God's rule (Ps. 2:2-3)? ___*rebellion*___

2. Although men are sinful, the framers of the Constitution believed that men have a God-given capacity to govern and be governed. Indeed, the Bible says that the ruler is God's "minister" (Rom. 13:4). Governments are His instruments to restrain evil and promote good.

   • What ability has God given mankind (Ps. 8:4-8)? ___*dominion over the earth*___

   • What did Israel want from its ruler (I Sam. 8:19-20)? ___*justice and defense*___

   • What roles did God fill as Israel's ruler (Isa. 33:22)? ___*judge, lawgiver, king*___

   • Whom should rulers punish (I Pet. 2:13-14)? ___*evildoers*___

   • What did Christ say we owe our rulers (Mark 12:13-17)? ___*tribute/taxes*___

   • What did Peter say we owe our rulers (I Pet. 2:17)? ___*honor*___

3. Madison believed that God is sovereign and the source of all law. He said the success of America depended on obedience to God, not the government: "We have staked the whole future of American civilization, not upon the power of government, far from it. We have staked the future of all our political institutions upon the capacity of each and all of us to govern ourselves, to sustain ourselves according to the Ten Commandments of God."

   • Who ordains rulers (Rom. 13:1)? ___*God*___

   • Who guides rulers' decisions (Prov. 21:1)? ___*the Lord*___

   • Who overthrows governments (Dan. 2:20-21)? ___*God*___

   • What brings ridicule to any nation (Prov. 14:34)? ___*sin*___

   • What brings blessing to any nation (Ps. 33:12)? ___*righteousness*___

   • What does God say about trusting men for help (Jer. 17:5, 7)? ___*It brings a curse.*___

American Republic

Chapter 7   Activity C

Write Your Own Encyclopedia Entry

Complete the following encyclopedia entry on the "Articles of Confederation."

In 1777 the Second Continental Congress drafted the (1) _Articles of Confederation   p. 112_ , but the states did not (2) _____ratify   p. 113_____ , or formally approve, the new system of government until the War for Independence was almost over. The last major state to accept the plan was (3) _____Virginia   p. 114_____ . The weak (4) _Confederation   pp. 113-14_ Congress, which began in 1781, passed laws but had no (5) _____executive   p. 118_____ branch or judicial branch. Although it had power to raise an (6) _____army   p. 114_____ to defend the country, it did *not* have power to (7) _tax   p. 114_ the states to pay its own expenses. Although Congress received control over all land claims in the (8) _____West   p. 114_____ , each of the thirteen states reserved the right to make separate agreements governing domestic and foreign (9) _trade   p. 114_ , such as tariffs.

The Congress's most lasting achievement involved the (10) _____Northwest   p. 114_____ Territory north of the Ohio River. An ordinance in 1785 created six-mile-square areas, called (11) _townships   pp. 114-15_ . These lands were sold in sections, each containing a total of (12) _____640   p. 115_____ acres, at a minimum price of one dollar per acre. A later ordinance provided for government in the region by dividing the new land into separate (13) _territories   p. 116_ , each with its own governor appointed by (14) _Congress   p. 116_ .

The confederation's weaknesses were embarrassing. The country of (15) _Britain   p. 119_ was angered by the mistreatment of Loyalists, and Spain tried to deny American traders the right of (16) _deposit   pp. 119-20_ . A rebellion of Massachusetts farmers, led by (17) _Daniel Shays   p. 120_ in 1786, was the last straw that brought an outcry for reform. The men who gathered at the (18) _Philadelphia/Constitutional   pp. 125, 127_ Convention in 1787 agreed to create a completely new form of government. They elected (19) _George Washington   pp. 122-23_ to be their chairman. After two years of debate, the states established a government by elected representatives, called a (20) _republic   p. 125_ .

American Republic

Chapter 7   Activity D

Who Am I?

Read each phrase and decide the person it describes. Write the correct answer in the blank.

John Jay   p. 120   1. treaty maker who negotiated with Spain

James Madison   p. 123   2. Father of the Constitution

Benjamin Franklin   p. 123   3. oldest delegate at the Constitutional Convention

Alexander Hamilton   p. 124   4. New York delegate who favored a strong government

Roger Sherman   pp. 127-29   5. shoemaker who introduced the Connecticut Compromise

Where Am I?

Read each phrase and decide the place it describes. Write the correct answer in the blank.

Ohio River   p. 114   6. southern boundary of the Northwest Territory

Northwest Territory   p. 117   7. territory where slavery was banned in 1787

New Orleans   pp. 119-20   8. Spanish port that denied Americans the right of deposit

p. 120   _Springfield, Massachusetts_   9. federal arsenal threatened by Shays's Rebellion

Mount Vernon   pp. 121-22   10. house where four states discussed trade disputes (1785)

Annapolis   p. 122   11. city where five states requested a better union (1786)

Independence Hall   p. 122   12. building where the Constitution was drafted (1787)

Virginia   p. 127   13. state that proposed the Large State Plan

New Jersey   p. 127   14. state that proposed the Small State Plan

Connecticut   p. 127   15. state that proposed the Great Compromise

What Am I?

Read each phrase and decide the thing it describes. Write the correct answer in the blank.

confederation   p. 112   16. a loose association or league of states

right of deposit   pp. 119-20   17. freedom to stockpile goods at a port until transported

tribute   p. 119   18. money paid to protect ships from harassment

Spirit of the Laws   p. 125   19. book about government written by the Frenchman Montesquieu

census   p. 127   20. a count of the population

The Federalist Papers   p. 129   21. series of essays favoring the adoption of the Constitution

electoral college   p. 129   22. constitutional system to elect the president

Bill of Rights   p. 129   23. first ten amendments to the Constitution

American Republic

Simple Outlining

Write a word or short phrase summarizing the topic of each section in the Constitution.

Preamble

Article I: The Legislative Branch

   1. Bicameral System of Legislature

   2. Composition of the House of Representatives

   3. Composition of the Senate

   4. Dates of Elections and Assembly

   5. *House Rules and Records   p. 140*

   6. *Salaries   pp. 140-41*

   7. *Procedure for Passing Bills   p. 141*

   8. *Enumerated Powers of Congress   pp. 142-44*

   9. *Powers Denied to Congress   pp. 144-45*

  10. *Powers Denied to the States   p. 145*

Article II: The Executive Branch

   1. *Election of the President   pp. 146-47*

   2. *Powers of the President   p. 148*

   3. *Duties of the President   p. 149*

   4. *Process of Impeachment   p. 149*

Article III: The Judicial Branch

   1. *Appointment of Judges   p. 149*

   2. *Jurisdiction of Federal Courts   pp. 149-50*

   3. *Treason   p. 150*

Article IV: Interstate Relations

   1. *Full Faith and Credit Among States   p. 151*

   2. *Mutual Duties of States   p. 151*

   3. *New States and Territories   pp. 151-52*

   4. *Duties of the Federal Government to the States   p. 152*

Article V: Amending the Constitution

Article VI: Constitutional and National Supremacy

Article VII: Ratifying the Constitution

American Republic

Chapter 8   Activity B

Qualifications and Terms of Office

Complete the chart. (Hint: Three blanks should say "none.")

Office	Minimum Age	Citizenship	Residency	Term of Office
representative	25 years *p. 137*	7 years *p. 137*	state represented *p. 137*	2 years *p. 137*
senator	30 years *p. 139*	9 years *p. 139*	state represented *p. 139*	6 years *p. 138*
president	35 years *p. 147*	natural-born *p. 147*	in U.S. for 14 years *p. 147*	4 years *p. 146*
justice	none *p. 149*	none *p. 149*	none *p. 149*	life *p. 149*

Division of Powers

Place a check under each branch that has the powers described below.

	Powers	House	Senate	President	Supreme Court
Legislation	originate bills involving money	✓ *p. 141*			
	make laws	✓ *p. 137*	✓ *p. 137*		
	veto laws			✓ *p. 141*	
	override vetoes	✓ *p. 141*	✓ *p. 141*		
	enforce laws			✓ *p. 149*	
	interpret laws				✓ *p. 149*
Diplomacy	declare war	✓ *p. 143*	✓ *p. 143*		
	raise armies	✓ *p. 143*	✓ *p. 143*		
	command armies			✓ *p. 148*	
	make treaties			✓ *p. 148*	
	approve treaties		✓ *p. 148*		
	appoint ambassadors and judges			✓ *p. 148*	
	approve ambassadors and judges		✓ *p. 148*		
Justice	impeachment of major federal officials	✓ *p. 138*			
	trial of impeachment cases		✓ *p. 139*		
	jurisdiction in cases involving a state				✓ *p. 150*

American Republic

Chapter 8   Activity C

Limited Federal Government

Our federal system is described in Article I, Sections 8-10; Article VI; and Amendment X. The national and state governments *share* some powers, some powers are reserved to one or the other, and some powers are *denied* both. Place a check under the place where the power resides, according to the *original* U.S. Constitution and Bill of Rights. (Hint: Some powers that were denied the national government were *not* denied the states at first.)

Powers	National	State	Neither
power to tax	✓ p. 142	✓ p. 157	
power to borrow money	✓ p. 142	✓ p. 157	
power to regulate trade with foreign countries	✓ pp. 142, 145		
power to regulate naturalization	✓ p. 142		
power to coin money	✓ pp. 142, 145		
power to declare war	✓ pp. 143, 145		
power to raise armies and navies	✓ pp. 143, 145		
power to suspend the writ of habeas corpus at any time		✓ pp. 144, 157	
power to pass a bill of attainder			✓ pp. 144-45
power to pass an ex post facto law			✓ pp. 144-45
power to tax exports for revenue			✓ pp. 144-45
power to grant titles of nobility			✓ p. 145
power to make treaties	✓ pp. 145, 148		
power to admit new states to the Union	✓ p. 151		
power to ratify amendments to the Constitution		✓ p. 152	
power to establish a state-sponsored church		✓ pp. 155, 157	
power to abridge freedom of speech and of the press		✓ pp. 155, 157	
power to enter homes without a search warrant		✓ pp. 155, 157	
power to compel a witness to testify against himself		✓ pp. 156-57	
power to subpoena witnesses	✓ p. 156	✓ p. 157	

Answer these questions about changes that later amendments made in government powers.

1. Name one power that the national government has gained. *Answers will vary. (income tax, etc.)* p. 160

2. Name one power that the national government has lost. *Answers will vary. (poll tax, etc.)* p. 165

3. Name one power that the state governments have lost. *Answers will vary. (due process, etc.)* p. 159

American Republic

Unscramble the Answer

Below is a list of definitions. Beside each definition write the correct term in the blanks. Then unscramble the double-underlined letters to complete the statement at the bottom.

p. 137	1. introduction to the Constitution	P r e a m b l e
p. 142	2. inability to pay creditors	b a n k r u p t c y
p. 165	3. tax on voters	p o l l t a x
p. 142	4. process of gaining citizenship	n a t u r a l i z a t i o n
p. 140	5. journal of Congress's activities	C o n g r e s s i o n a l R e c o r d
p. 144	6. retroactive law	e x p o s t f a c t o l a w
p. 148	7. complete forgiveness of a crime	p a r d o n
p. 142	8. making illegal copies of money	c o u n t e r f e i t i n g
p. 139	9. Senate leader	p r e s i d e n t p r o t e m p o r e
p. 137	10. two-house legislative system	b i c a m e r a l s y s t e m
p. 144	11. prisoner's right to be charged	w r i t o f h a b e a s c o r p u s
p. 141	12. automatic veto	p o c k e t v e t o
p. 150	13. aid and comfort to enemies	t r e a s o n
p. 162	14. right to vote	s u f f r a g e
p. 150	15. court's right to hear a case first	o r i g i n a l j u r i s d i c t i o n
p. 142	16. protection of an author's works	c o p y r i g h t
p. 138	17. House leader	S p e a k e r o f t h e H o u s e
p. 137	18. counting of the population	c e n s u s

The Constitution's success rests on the principle of ___separation___ of ___powers___ p. 135 .

Definitions

Write a definition for each of these special terms.

19. Bill of Rights ___the first ten amendments that secured personal liberties   p. 155___

20. due process of law ___guarantee of a fair and proper trial   p. 159___

21. quorum ___the minimum number of members of a group needed to transact business   p. 140___

22. subpoena ___document requiring a witness to appear in court   p. 156___

23. change of venue ___movement of a trial to a new location to ensure fairness   p. 150___

Skill: Recognition

American Republic

Chapter 8   Activity E

Unconstitutional Laws and Actions

You are a young federal judge. Write a *C* in the blank if the hypothetical case is constitutional and a *U* if the action is unconstitutional. In the blank at the right, give the article and section or the amendment in the U.S. Constitution that supports your conclusion.

Example:

__U__ Maine has elected a man who is only twenty-four years old to the U.S. House of Representatives.   ___Art. I, Sec. 2___

__U__ 1. The U.S. representatives have voted to extend their terms to four years.   ___Art. I, Sec. 2___

__C__ 2. The House of Representatives has set its membership at 435.   ___Art. I, Sec. 2___

__U__ 3. The House recently sent a federal official to jail after he was impeached for treason.   ___Art. I, Sec. 3___

__U__ 4. The Senate has voted to ban the vice president from its chambers.   ___Art. I, Sec. 3___

__C__ 5. Congress has passed a law requiring all states to hold congressional elections on the Tuesday following the first Monday in November.   ___Art. I, Sec. 4___

__U__ 6. The Supreme Court has ordered the Senate to change its procedural rules because they give unfair advantages to older members.   ___Art. I, Sec. 5___

__C__ 7. The House has limited the power of its Speaker to control proceedings.   ___Art. I, Sec. 5___

__U__ 8. A U.S. senator accused of libel was arrested on his way to the Senate.   ___Art. I, Sec. 6___

__U__ 9. The president pro tempore has been appointed to a civil office in the Agricultural Department.   ___Art. I, Sec. 6___

__U__ 10. The Senate has proposed a revenue bill to pay for a new highway.   ___Art. I, Sec. 7___

__C__ 11. A recent bill automatically became law after ten days because the president never signed it or vetoed it.   ___Art. I, Sec. 7___

__U__ 12. Congress overrode the president's last veto by a simple majority in both houses.   ___Art. I, Sec. 7___

__C__ 13. Congress has banned imports from China.   ___Art. I, Sec. 8___

__C__ 14. Congress has limited the length of copyrights to the lifetime of the author plus seventy years.   ___Art. I, Sec. 8___

__C__ 15. Congress is using Alabama's militia to enforce a new law in the state, against the wishes of the governor.   ___Art. I, Sec. 8___

__U__ 16. Congress has given Miami the privilege of being a "free port" where no tariffs apply.   ___Art. I, Sec. 9___

__U__ 17. Alaska has decided to coin its own money to help pay its debts.   ___Art. I, Sec. 10___

__U__ 18. Kansas has passed an ex post facto law that fines doctors who have performed abortions in the past five years.   ___Art. I, Sec. 10___

_U_ 19. Five states in the Deep South have entered into a confederation for mutual defense, without the approval of Congress. _Art. I, Sec. 10_

_U_ 20. Texas has declared war on Mexico because of illegal drug traffic. _Art. I, Sec. 10_

_C_ 21. The House of Representatives picked the U.S. president because none of the candidates received a majority of the electors' votes. _Art. II, Sec. 1_

_U_ 22. The new U.S. president was born a German citizen, but he has been an American citizen for fourteen years. _Art. II, Sec. 1_

_C_ 23. If both the president and vice president die, Congress has decided that the Speaker of the House will become the new president. _Art. II, Sec. 1_

_U_ 24. Congress has voted to decrease the president's salary during this term. _Art. II, Sec. 1_

_C_ 25. The president has granted pardons to three federal officials who were convicted of embezzlement against the U.S. Treasury. _Art. II, Sec. 2_

_U_ 26. The Senate has removed the president as the commander in chief of the army because he lacks experience and ability. _Art. II, Sec. 2_

_U_ 27. Congress has voted to require the president to receive its approval when he removes the head of an executive department. _Art. II, Sec. 2_

_U_ 28. At the president's request, Congress has voted to remove all Supreme Court justices over the age of seventy-five. _Art. III, Sec. 1_

_U_ 29. According to a new congressional law, treason includes refusal to pay income taxes. _Art. III, Sec. 3_

_U_ 30. Illinois does not give full faith and credit to marriage licenses from New Mexico. _Art. IV, Sec. 1_

_U_ 31. Congress has formed a new state within the jurisdiction of California without the consent of California's legislature. _Art. IV, Sec. 3_

_C_ 32. Three-fourths of the state legislatures have ratified a new amendment making abortion illegal. _Art. V_

_U_ 33. Congress has passed a law barring churches from preaching the gospel. _Amend. I_

_U_ 34. Congress has passed a law forbidding the publication of attacks against government officials. _Amend. I_

_C_ 35. Congress has passed a new law forcing convicted criminals to work for the government without pay. _Amend. XIII_

_C_ 36. Congress has introduced a tax on incomes that does not apply equally to all U.S. citizens. _Amend. XVI_

_U_ 37. A state has denied the right of women to vote. _Amend. XIX_

_U_ 38. A state requires all voters to pay a poll tax. _Amend. XXIV_

_U_ 39. Congress has raised the voting age to twenty-one. _Amend. XXVI_

_U_ 40. Both houses of Congress have voted to give themselves a pay raise this session. _Amend. XXVII_

American Republic

Chapter 9   Activity A

Foreign/Domestic Time Line    *Classroom discussion*

The new government under the U.S. Constitution experienced major challenges, both domestic and foreign. As you read the chapter, list the major events that took place each year at home and abroad. (You should find at least twenty major events.)

Domestic Events	Year	Foreign Events	
Washington's inauguration p. 170 cabinet established p. 171 Judiciary Act (federal district courts) p. 174	1789	start of the French Revolution p. 176	
Funding Bill p. 173 Assumption Act p. 173	1790		
Bank of the United States established p. 173 Bill of Rights ratified p. 175 Vermont admitted as a state p. 175	1791		
Kentucky admitted as a state p. 175	1792		
	1793	French war with Britain p. 177 Washington's Neutrality Proclamation Genêt affair pp. 177-78	p. 177
Whiskey Rebellion p. 174 Battle of Fallen Timbers p. 175	1794	Jay Treaty with Britain	
peace of Fort Greenville p. 175	1795	peace talks with Britain on impressment Pinckney Treaty with Spain p. 179	p. 178
Tennessee admitted as a state p. 175 Washington's "Farewell Address" p. 179 election of John Adams pp. 180-81	1796	start of "quasi war" with France	
	1797		
Alien and Sedition Acts p. 186 Virginia and Kentucky Resolutions p. 187	1798	XYZ affair revealed	
	1799	Napoleon begins rule of France p. 186	
disputed election of Jefferson p. 188	1800	convention with France p. 186	
appointment of Chief Justice Marshall p. 189 Judiciary Act (midnight judges) p. 190 Marbury v. Madison (judicial review) p. 190	1801		

American Republic

Chapter 9   Activity B

Words You Need to Know: Precedent   ☆ *Classroom discussion*

The actions of America's first leaders became precedents (examples for future actions). As you read the chapter, look for the important precedents. Then for each situation below, describe what precedents were set, when they were set, and who set them.

Situation	Precedent(s)	Year	Person(s) Responsible
Washington's inauguration	*left hand on the Bible and right hand raised; end with "so help me God"*	*1789*	*George Washington*
need to organize the executive departments	*establishment of the cabinet; departments of state, treasury, defense, and justice p. 171*	*1789*	*George Washington (James Madison)*
need to give the chief executive a title	*official title—"President of the United States"; customary title—"Mr. President" p. 173*	*1789*	*House of Representatives*
need for a source of federal revenue	*raising revenue with tariffs and excise taxes p. 172*	*1789*	*Alexander Hamilton*
need to honor war debts	*America's determination to maintain good credit (Funding Bill; Washington's "Farewell Address") pp. 173-74; 179-80*	*1790*	*Alexander Hamilton (George Washington)*
desire for a national bank	*Bank of the United States (to handle the nation's finances) p. 173*	*1791*	*Alexander Hamilton*
disputes between political factions	*two-party political system (Federalist and Democratic-Republican) p. 174*	*1792*	*Alexander Hamilton/ Thomas Jefferson*
need to stop the Whiskey Rebellion	*president's use of federal force to support national laws p. 174*	*1794*	*George Washington*
need for a federal court system	*chief justice; thirteen federal district courts; three circuit appeals courts (Judiciary Act) pp. 174-75*	*1789*	*Congress*
demand for long-term alliances in foreign wars	*policy of isolationism (Neutrality Proclamation) p. 177*	*1793*	*George Washington*
House's attempt to restrict monies for the Jay Treaty	*House's policy not to interfere with presidential treaties p. 178*	*1795*	*George Washington*
desire to see Washington run for a third term	*tradition of a two-term presidency p. 179*	*1796*	*George Washington*
states' efforts to overrule the Alien and Sedition Acts	*assertion of the right of nullification (Virginia and Kentucky Resolutions) pp. 186-87*	*1798*	*James Madison/ Thomas Jefferson*
lack of unity in Supreme Court decisions	*private conferences; majority and dissenting opinions p. 189*	*1801*	*John Marshall*
an unconstitutional federal law taken to court	*Supreme Court's power of judicial review (Marbury v. Madison) p. 190*	*1801*	*John Marshall*

American Republic

Government Then and Now (Exploring the *World Almanac*)

Our government has changed in many ways. With the help of your text and the *World Almanac* (or other library resource), see how many facts you can find about the salaries of officials and the size and leadership of our government under Washington and now. Also try to answer the questions below.

Salaries

Individual	Salary Then p. 172	Salary Now
President	$25,000/year	in almanac
Cabinet Member	$3,500/year	
Speaker	$12/day	
Representative	$6/day	
Senator	$6/day	
Justice	$3,500/year	

Size

Branch	Size Then	Size Now
Cabinet	4 p. 171	14
House	65	435
Senate	26	100
Supreme Court	6 p. 175	9

Leadership

Office	First Office Holder pp. 171, 175	Current Office Holder
President	George Washington	See a current almanac.
Vice President	John Adams	
Speaker of the House	Frederick Muhlenberg	
Chief Justice	John Jay	
Secretary of State	Thomas Jefferson	
Secretary of the Treasury	Alexander Hamilton	
Attorney General	Edmund Randolph	
Secretary of War (Defense)	Henry Knox	

1. How long has the U.S. Constitution been in force? __*The year 1989 was its 200th anniversary.*__

2. How many presidents has the United States had? __*Clinton was the forty-second.*__

3. What is the U.S. government's yearly expenditure (versus $600,000 at first)? ____
   over $1.5 trillion

4. What is the current federal employment of civilians (versus 800 at first)? __*nearly 3 million*__

5. List the current cabinet posts. __*State, Treasury, Defense, Attorney General, Interior,*__
   Agriculture, Labor, Commerce, Housing and Urban Development, Transportation, Energy,
   Health and Human Services, Education, Veterans Affairs

American Republic

Abigail Adams's Letter About Washington, D.C.

Abigail Adams was the first wife of a president to live in Washington, D.C., which was still under construction. Read Mrs. Adams's letter to her daughter, dated November 21, 1800. Then answer the questions.

I arrived here on Sunday last, and without meeting with any accident worth noticing, except losing ourselves when we left Baltimore. . . ; woods are all you see, from Baltimore until you reach the city, which is only so in name. Here and there is a small cot, without a glass window, interspersed among the forests, through which you travel miles without seeing any human being. . . .

The [Potomac] river, which runs up to Alexandria, is in full view of my window, and I see the vessels as they pass and repass. The house is upon a grand and superb scale, requiring about thirty servants to attend and keep the apartments in proper order, and perform the ordinary business of the house and stables; an establishment very well proportioned to the President's salary. The lighting of apartments, from the kitchen to parlors and chambers, is a tax [difficulty] indeed; and the fires we are obliged to keep to secure us from daily agues [chills] is another very cheering comfort. To assist us in this great castle, and render less attendance necessary, bells are wholly wanting, not one single one being hung through the whole house, and promises are all you can obtain. This is so great an inconvenience that I know not what to do, or

how to do. . . . If they will put me up some bells, and let me have wood enough to keep fires, I design [plan] to be pleased.

I could content myself almost anywhere three months; but, surrounded with forests, can you believe that wood is not to be had, because people cannot be found to cut and cart it! . . . We have indeed come into a new country.

You must keep all this to yourself, and when asked how I like it, say that I write you the situation is beautiful, which is true. The house is made habitable, but there is not a single apartment finished, and all withinside, except the plastering, has been done since Briesler came. We have not the least fence, yard, or other convenience, without, and the great unfinished audience room I make a drying room of, to hang up the clothes in. The principal stairs are not up, and will not be this winter. . . .

It is a beautiful spot, capable of every improvement, and, the more I view it the more I am delighted with it. . . . Adieu, my dear. Give my love to your brother, and tell him he is ever present upon my mind.

1. What was the most striking feature of the countryside to Mrs. Adams? __*extensive forest*__

2. List five problems she faced. __*getting lost, solitude, poor lighting, lack of bells,*__
   __*lack of wood, unfinished rooms, lack of fences and yards, unfinished stairs*__

3. What positive things did she say about the place? __*view of river, scale of house, beauty of*__
   __*the location, great possibilities*__

4. Why did she tell her daughter not to mention the hardships? __*Answers will vary.*__
   __*Abigail Adams felt it was her duty not to appear discontent. She knew that the hardships*__
   __*were only temporary.*__

American Republic

Chapter 9   Activity E

What God Says About Honor

One reason for our country's success is the example the first presidents set. They placed the needs of the nation above personal gain. With the help of your Bible, answer these questions.

1. In his "Farewell Address," Washington quoted his life maxim: "Honesty is always the best policy." He said that the two "great pillars of human happiness" are "religion and morality." He warned against "cunning, ambitious, and unprincipled men" who used party strife to take over government.

   • What are two traits of a good ruler (Exod. 18:21)? __ability, godly fear, truthfulness, etc.__

   • What is the most important source of honor (John 5:44)? __God, not men__

   • What character trait precedes honor (Prov. 18:12)? __humility__

   • What type of person should not be given a place of honor (Prov. 26:1)? __a fool__

2. In a letter to his wife, President John Adams expressed his dislike of party "jealousies and rivalries." He said, "If the Federalists go to playing pranks, I will resign the office, and let Jefferson lead." The test of Adams's character came when his party and country demanded war with France. His commitment to peace cost him his popularity and his reelection.

   • What could be a good reason for a ruler to avoid war (Luke 14:28-32)? _____
   __if defeat is likely__

   • Why did Jonathan give up his crown (I Sam. 16:1; 18:1-4)? __love of God's chosen king__

   • What should a good ruler *not* do (Deut. 16:19)? __twist justice, be partial, or take bribes__

   • What is the source of true greatness (Matt. 20:25-28)? __service to others__

3. After the appointment of "the midnight judges," Adams and Jefferson stopped speaking to each other. Later, Abigail Adams broke the ice by sending Jefferson a note of sympathy after the death of his daughter. He replied that honest differences in political convictions should never be permitted to disturb the two men's lifetime friendship and mutual esteem. The two political enemies renewed their friendship until their deaths.

   • What two traits preserve a ruler (Prov. 20:28)? __mercy and truth__

   • What gives stability to government (Prov. 16:12)? __righteousness__

   • What attitude prevents strife (Phil. 2:3)? __lowliness of mind; higher esteem of others__

4. Jefferson tried to reassure his Federalist opponents in his inaugural speech: "Let us, then, fellow citizens, unite with one heart and one mind. . . . We have called by different names brethren of the same principle. We are all republicans—we are all federalists."

   • How should we treat our opponents (Rom. 12:14-21)? __live peaceably__

   • What brings a man honor (Prov. 20:3)? __to cease from strife__

   • What destroys a nation (Mark 3:24)? __division against itself__

   • What helps a nation survive (Prov. 29:18)? __revelation from God; respect for law__

American Republic

Interview with John Adams

Pretend you are John Adams. The day after Jefferson's inauguration in 1801 you have an interview with a writer from a famous newspaper. How would you answer these questions?

1. Where do you plan to retire? __my farm in Braintree, Massachusetts   pp. 182-84__

2. What was your greatest accomplishment? __Convention of 1800   p. 186__

3. What is the most important advice you would give to the new president? __Answers will vary.__

4. What experience best prepared you for the presidency? __Answers will vary. (diplomat, etc.)__   p. 181

5. Did you enjoy being Washington's vice president? __It's the most insignificant office ever contrived.   p. 181__

6. How difficult was it to follow Washington as president? __Answers will vary.__
__(I never sought or expected popularity. I could never be George Washington.)   p. 181__

7. Why were the Federalists so unenthusiastic about your reelection? __Answers will vary.__
__(I opposed their efforts to abuse power and the popular call to arms against France.)   pp. 185-88__

8. What do you think is the most important character trait a president needs? __a desire to serve others   p. 184__

9. How helpful has your wife, Abigail, been during your work? __Answers will vary.__
__(She was the delight of my heart, the sweetener of my toils, etc.)   pp. 181-84__

10. What future do you foresee for your son, John Quincy? __Answers will vary. (president)__
__pp. 184-85__

11. What was your reaction to the XYZ affair? __Answers will vary.__
__(I was outraged. I presented the case to Congress as a lawyer would.)   p. 185__

12. Why didn't you declare war on France? What did you do instead? __Answers will vary. (I didn't believe our young republic was prepared for war. The navy became a separate department, Congress voted to build forty ships, and the size of the army was tripled.)   pp. 185-86__

13. Why didn't you support the Alien and Sedition Acts? __Answers will vary. (They were an abuse of power for party ends and were dangerously vague. The Sedition Act was unconstitutional.)   p. 186__

14. Why did you choose John Marshall to be chief justice of the Supreme Court? __Answers will vary. (I wanted a strong leader who would strengthen the courts.)   p. 189__

15. Do you believe "the midnight judges" were unconstitutional? __No__ Why? __Answers will vary. (The law gave me the power, and the Senate could reject them.)   p. 190__

American Republic

Map Study: Growth and Conflicts

Refer to the maps in the textbook on pages 646-47, 200, and 209 to complete the map on the back.

1. Label these bodies of water:

   Rivers—Potomac, Tippecanoe, Mississippi, Missouri, Arkansas, Yellowstone, Columbia
   Lakes—Champlain, Ontario, Erie, Michigan

2. Label these new states: Vermont (1791), Kentucky (1792), Tennessee (1796), Ohio (1803), Louisiana (1812).

3. Label these cities and forts: Washington, D.C.; Detroit; New Orleans; St. Louis; Ft. McHenry.

4. Using three colored pencils, color these three things:

   • the boundaries of the Louisiana Purchase
   • the route of the Lewis and Clark expedition
   • the routes of the Pike expeditions

5. Draw these figures at the appropriate places:

    Pike's Peak   *p. 200 (map)*   Perry's naval victory   *p. 210*

    Battle of Tippecanoe   *p. 207*   ⚔ militia's defeat at Bladensburg   *p. 211*

   🏳 brave defense of Baltimore fort   *p. 211*   🗡 Jackson's greatest victory   *p. 212*

Map Questions

Answer these questions based on the maps in the textbook on pages 646-47 and 200.

1. What town was the starting point for western expeditions? __*St. Louis*__

2. What rivers did Lewis and Clark follow? __*Missouri, Yellowstone, Columbia, [Snake]*__

3. What rivers did Pike's second expedition follow? __*Arkansas and Rio Grande*__

4. Based on the scale, how many miles did Lewis and Clark travel one way? __*about 2,000*__

5. Based on the scale, how many miles did Pike travel one way on his first trip? __*about 600*__

6. Based on the scale, how many miles did Pike travel to reach Pike's Peak? __*about 1,000*__

7. Why might your estimates be about half what they should be? __*Rivers aren't straight.*__

8. If Lewis traveled 8,000 miles and spent $40,000, what was his cost per mile? __*$5*__

9. Brain Teaser—Name the modern states that Lewis and Clark crossed. __*Missouri, Kansas,*__
   __*Nebraska, Iowa, South Dakota, North Dakota, Montana, Idaho, Oregon, Washington*__

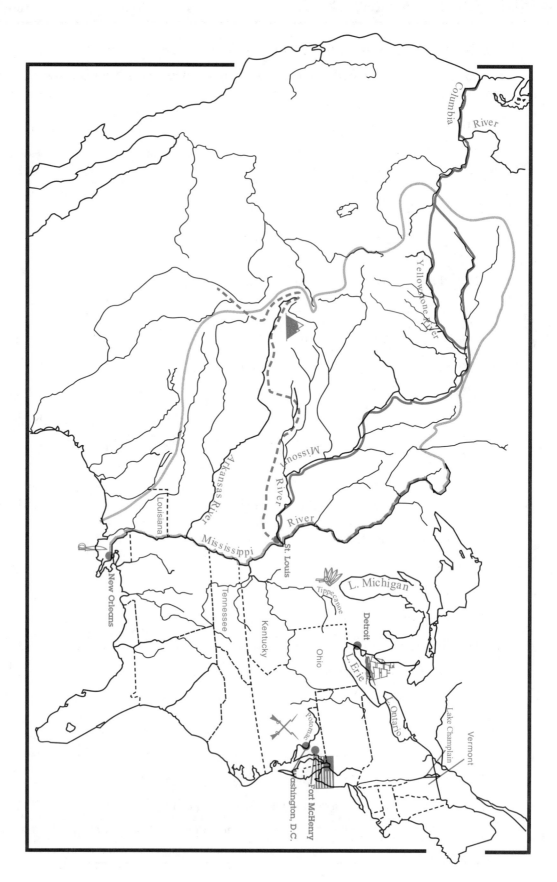

Columbia River

Yellowstone River

Missouri River

Arkansas River

Louisiana

Mississippi

St. Louis

New Orleans

Tippecanoe

L. Michigan

Tennessee

Kentucky

Detroit

Ohio

L. Erie

L. Ontario

Potomac

Lake Champlain

Vermont

Fort McHenry

Washington, D.C.

American Republic

The Journals of Lewis and Clark (May 14, 1804–September 24, 1806)

The journals of Lewis and Clark are filled with exciting stories. Both officers kept a daily journal of the trip. Along with their adventures and discoveries, we can see their leadership skills and their endurance through many hardships. As you read these excerpts, list five dates that tell about each topic below. Then answer the questions at the end of the activity.

Hardships   _Oct. 9, 1804; June 12, June 15, June 29, Aug. 14, Sept. 18, 1805; Mar. 23, 1806_

Leadership skills _May 17, Aug. 20, Oct. 13, 1804; June 28, 1805; Aug. 8, Aug. 14, 1806; Mar. 23, 1806_

Bears (grizzly bears)   _Apr. 13, Apr. 29, May 5, May 6, June 28, 1805_

Sacajawea   _Feb. 11, June 12, June 15, June 29, Aug. 8, Aug. 14, Aug. 17, 1805_

from Clark's Journal

[May 14, 1804] Rained the fore part of the day. I set out at 4 o'clock, P.M., in the presence of many of the neighboring inhabitants and proceeded under a gentle breeze up the Missouri to the upper point of the first island, 4 miles, and camped on the island.

[May 17, 1804] A fair day. Compelled to punish [two enlisted men] for misconduct.

[August 19] Sergeant Floyd is taken very bad all at once with a bilious colic [appendicitis?]. We attempt to relieve him without success as yet. He gets worse and we are much alarmed at his situation. All attention to him.

[August 20] Sergeant Floyd as bad as he can be, no pulse, and nothing will stay a moment on his stomach or bowels. . . . Sergeant Floyd died with a great deal of composure. We buried him on the top of the bluff a half mile below a small river to which we gave his name. After paying all the honor to our deceased brother, we camped in the mouth of Floyd's River, about 30 yards wide. A beautiful evening.

[October 9] The day continued cold and windy. Some rain. Sorry. Canoes of skins passed down from the two villages a short distance above, and many [Mandan Indians] came to view us all day, much astonished at my black servant, who did not lose the opportunity of displaying his powers, strength, &c.

[October 13] One man, J. Newman, confined for mutinous expression. Set out early. Passed a camp of Sioux. Those people only viewed us and did not speak one word. We tried the prisoner Newman last night by 9 of his peers. They did "sentence him 75 lashes and disbanded him from the party."

[November 4] A fine morning. We continued to cut down trees and raise our houses [at Fort Mandan]. A Mr. Charbonneau, interpreter for the Gros Ventre nation, came to see us. This man wished to hire as an interpreter. Great numbers of Indians pass, hunting.

from Lewis's Journal

[February 11, 1805] The weather was fair and cold. Wind N.W. About five o'clock this evening, one of the wives of Charbonneau was delivered of a fine boy. It is worthy of remark that this was the first child which this woman had born, and as is common in such cases her labor was tedious and the pain violent.

[April 13] We saw many tracks of the white bear of enormous size, along the river shore. We have not as yet seen one of these animals, though their tracks are so abundant and recent. The men, as well as ourselves, are anxious to meet with some of these bear. The Indians give a very formidable account of the strength and ferocity of this animal, which they never dare to attack but in parties of six, eight, or ten persons; and are even then frequently defeated with the loss of one or more of their party.

[April 29] Set out this morning at the usual hour. About 8 A.M. we fell in with two brown or yellow bear, both of which we wounded. One of them made his escape; the other, after my firing on him, pursued me 70 or 80 yards but fortunately had been so badly wounded that he was unable to pursue so closely as to prevent my charging my gun. We again repeated our fire, and killed him.

. . . It is a much more furious and formidable animal [than the black bear], and will frequently pursue the hunter when wounded. The Indians may well fear this animal, equipped as they generally are with their bows and arrows or indifferent fusees [muskets]; but in the hands of skillful riflemen, they are by no means as formidable or dangerous as they have been presented.

[May 5] Captain Clark and Drouillard killed the largest brown bear this evening which we have yet seen. It was a most tremendous-looking animal, and extremely hard to kill. Notwithstanding he had five balls through his lungs and five others in various parts, he swam more than half the distance across the river, to a sandbar, and it was at least twenty minutes before he died. He did not attempt to attack, but fled, and made the most tremendous roaring from the moment he was shot. We had no means of weighing this monster. Captain Clark thought he would weigh 500 pounds. For my own part, I think the estimate too small by 100 pounds. He measured 8 feet 7 1/2 inches from the nose to the extremity of the hind feet; 5 feet 10 1/2 inches around the breast; 1 foot 11 inches around the middle of the arm; and 3 feet 11 inches around the neck. His talons, which were five in number on each foot, were 4 3/8 inches in length. He was in good order.

We therefore divided him among the party, and made them boil the oil and put it in a cask for future use. The oil is as hard as hog's lard when cool—much more so than that of the black bear.

[May 6] Saw a brown bear swim the river above us; he disappeared before we could get in reach of him. I find that the curiosity of our party is pretty well satisfied with respect to this animal.

from Clark's Journal

[June 12] Saw a number of rattlesnakes today. One of the men caught one by the head, in catching hold of a bush on which his head lay reclined. Three canoes were in great danger today; one dipped water, another very near turned over, &c. The interpreter's woman very sick. One man has a felon rising on his hand; the other, with the toothache, has taken cold in the jaw, &c.

from Lewis's Journal *(He had gone ahead of the main party in search of the Great Falls.)*

[June 13] This morning we set out about sunrise after taking breakfast off our venison and fish. My ears were saluted with the agreeable sound of a fall of water, which soon began to make a roaring too tremendous to be mistaken for anything but the Great Falls of the Missouri. Here I arrived about 12 o'clock, having traveled about 15 miles. I hurried down the hill to gaze at this sublimely grand spectacle.

. . . The whole body of water passes with incredible swiftness. Immediately at the cascade, the river is about 300 yards wide. About 90 or 100 yards of this is a smooth even sheet of water falling over a precipice of at least 80 feet; the remaining part, about 200 yards wide, on my right, forms the grandest sight I ever beheld. The rocks seem to be most happily fixed to present a sheet of the whitest beaten froth for 200 yards in length and about 80 feet perpendicular. . . . From the reflection of the sun on the spray or mist which arises from these Falls, there is a beautiful rainbow produced which adds not a little to the beauty of this majestically grand scenery.

After writing this imperfect description, I again viewed the Falls, and was disgusted with the imperfect idea which it conveyed of the scene. I wished for the pencil of Salvator Rosa, a Titian, or the pen of Thomson, that I might be enabled to give to the enlightened world some just idea of this truly magnificent and sublimely grand object which has, from the commencement of time, been concealed from the view of civilized man. But this was fruitless and vain. I most sincerely regretted that I had not brought a camera obscura with me.

from Clark's Journal *(His party was carrying the boats up the river to meet Lewis.)*

[June 15] A fair morning, and warm. We set out at the usual time and proceeded with great difficulty, as the river is more rapid. Our Indian woman sick and low-spirited.

The current excessively rapid and difficult to ascend. Great numbers of dangerous places, and the fatigue which we have to encounter is incredible: the men in the water from morning until night, hauling the cord and boats, walking on sharp rocks and slippery stones which alternately cut their feet and throw them down. Notwithstanding all this difficulty, they go with great cheerfulness. Added to those difficulties, the rattlesnakes are innumerable and require great caution.

The Indian woman much worse this evening. She will not take any medicine. Her husband petitions to return, &c. River more rapid.

from Lewis's Journal

[June 25] Captain Clark somewhat unwell today. He made Charbonneau cook for the party against their return. It is worthy of remark that the winds are sometimes so strong on these plains that the men informed me that they hoisted a sail in the canoe and it had driven her along on the truck wheels. This is really sailing on dry land.

[June 28] The white bear have become so troublesome to us that I do not think it prudent to send one man alone on an errand of any kind, particularly where he has to pass through the brush. They come close around our camp every night but have never yet ventured to attack us, and our dog gives us timely notice of their visits. I have made the men sleep with their arms by them as usual, for fear of accidents.

from Clark's Journal

[June 29] A torrent of rain and hail fell, more violent than ever I saw before. The rain fell like one volley of water from the heavens and gave us time only to get out of the way of a torrent of water which was pouring down the hill into the river with immense force, tearing everything before it, taking with it large rocks and mud.

I took my gun and shot pouch in my left hand and with the right scrambled up the hill, pushing the interpreter's wife—who had her child in her arms—before me, the interpreter himself making attempts to pull up his wife by the hand, much scared and nearly without motion. We at length reached the top of the hill safely. I directed the party to return to the camp, at the run, as fast as possible to get to our load, where clothes could be got to cover the child, whose clothes were all lost; and the woman, who was but just recovering from a severe indisposition and was wet and cold, I was fearful of a relapse.

from Lewis's Journal

[August 8] The Indian woman recognized the point of a high plain to our right, which, she informed us, was not very distant from the summer retreat of her nation, on a river beyond the mountains which runs to the west. She assures us that we shall either find her people on this river, or on the river immediately west of its source.

As it is now all-important with us to meet with those people as soon as possible, I determined to proceed tomorrow with a small party to the source of the principal stream of this river and pass the mountains to the Columbia, and down that river until I found the Indians. In short, it is my resolution to find them or some others who have horses, if it should cause me a trip of one month. For, without horses we shall be obliged to leave a great part of our stores, of which it appears to me that we have a stock already sufficiently small for the length of the voyage before us.

[August 14] This evening Charbonneau struck his Indian woman, for which Captain Clark gave him a severe reprimand. Joseph and Reuben Fields killed 4 deer and an antelope. Captain Clark killed a buck. Several of the men have lamed themselves by various accidents in working the canoes through this difficult part of the river, and Captain Clark was obliged personally to assist them in this labor.

[August 17] Captain Clark arrived [at the Shoshone camp] with the interpreter, Charbonneau, and the Indian woman, who proved to be a sister of the chief Cameâhwait. The meeting of these people was really affecting, particularly between Sacajawea and an Indian woman who had been taken prisoner with her, and who had afterwards escaped and rejoined her nation.

[August 18] This day I completed my thirty-first year. I reflected that I had as yet done but little, very little, indeed, to further the happiness of the human race, or to advance the information of the succeeding generation. I viewed with regret the many hours I have spent in indolence. But, since they are past and cannot be recalled, I dash from me the gloomy thought, and resolve in future to redouble my efforts . . . to live for mankind, as I have heretofore lived for myself.

[September 18] We marched 18 miles this day and encamped on the side of a steep mountain. We suffered for water this day, passing one rivulet only. This morning we finished the remainder of our last colt. We dined and supped on a scant portion of portable soup, a few canisters of which, a little bear's oil, and about 20 pounds of candles form our stock of provision, the only resources being our guns and pack horses. Our route is along the ridge of a high mountain. Course S. 20 W. 18 miles. Used the snow for cooking.

from Clark's Journal

[November 7] Great joy in camp. We are in view of the ocean, this great Pacific Ocean which we have been so long anxious to see, and the roaring or noise made by the waves breaking on the rocky shores (as I suppose) may be heard distinctly.

from Lewis's Journal

[February 20, 1806] This forenoon we were visited by Tâhcum, a principal chief of the Chinooks, and 25 men of his nation. In the evening at sunset we desired them to depart, as is our custom, and closed our gates. We never suffer parties of such number to remain within the fort all night. We determined always to be on our guard as much as the nature of the situation will permit us, and never place ourselves at the mercy of any savages. We well know that the treachery of the aborigines of America and the too great confidence of our countrymen in their sincerity and friendship has caused the destruction of many hundreds of us.

from Clark's Journal

[March 23] At 1:00 P.M. left Fort Clatsop on our homeward-bound journey. At this place we had wintered and remained from the 7th of December, 1805, to this day, and have lived as well as we had any right to expect, and we can say that we were never one day without three meals of some kind a day, either poor elk meat or roots, notwithstanding the repeated fall of rain which has fallen almost constantly.

from Lewis's Journal

[September 23] We rose early. Descended to the Mississippi and down that river to St. Louis, at which place we arrived about 12 o'clock. We suffered the party to fire off their pieces as a salute to the town. We were met by all the village and received a hearty welcome from its inhabitants.

1. Who was the only person to die on this incredible two-year journey? ___*Sergeant Floyd*___

2. When was the last discipline problem mentioned? ___*October 13, 1804*___

3. When did Sacajawea give birth to her baby? ___*February 11, 1805*___

4. Lewis said grizzlies were not as dangerous as reported. Did his view change? ___*definitely*___

5. What do the journals usually call Sacajawea? ___*Indian or interpreter's woman*___

6. Give a date from Clark's journal that shows his concern for Sacajawea. ___*June 15 or 29, 1805*___

7. When did the exploration party come in view of the Pacific? ___*November 7, 1805*___

American Republic

Steps to War

Place these events in the order they appear in the textbook.

Battle of Tippecanoe
British victory at Trafalgar
Chesapeake affair
coalition of War Hawks

Embargo Act
issue of Orders in Council
Macon's Bill Number 2
Madison's declaration of war

Non-Intercourse Act
repeal of Milan Decree
repeal of Orders in Council
Tecumseh's confederation

1805 1. *British victory at Trafalgar   p. 202*

1807 2. *issue of Orders in Council   p. 202*

      3. *Chesapeake affair   p. 205*

      4. *Embargo Act   p. 205*

1809 5. *Non-Intercourse Act   pp. 205-6*

1810 6. *Macon's Bill Number 2   p. 206*

      7. *repeal of Milan Decree   p. 206*

      8. *Tecumseh's confederation   p. 206*

1811 9. *Battle of Tippecanoe   pp. 206-7*

     10. *coalition of War Hawks   p. 208*

1812 11. *Madison's declaration of war   p. 208*

     12. *repeal of Orders in Council   p. 208*

Major Battles

Complete the chart. For each battle, include the American commander if he is mentioned in the text. Also place an asterisk (*) beside each battle that the United States won.

	Battle	Year	Leader	Significance
Northern Campaigns	*Tippecanoe pp. 206-7	1811	William Henry Harrison	destruction of Tecumseh's Indian capital
	Detroit p. 208	1812	William Hull	loss of much of the Northwest
	Fort Niagara pp. 208-9	1812	none	disastrous defeat because the militia did not cooperate
	*Lake Erie p. 210	1813	Oliver Hazard Perry	recapture of Great Lakes and Northwest
Eastern Campaigns	*Plattsburg p. 211	1814	none	invasion of New York turned back
	Bladensburg p. 211	1814	none	rout of militia; British burning of the capital
	*Fort McHenry p. 211	1814	none	invasion of Chesapeake stopped; Baltimore saved
	*New Orleans pp. 211-12	1815	Andrew Jackson	America's biggest victory; protection of the Louisiana Territory

American Republic

Chapter 10   Activity D

Copyediting: Growing Pains of a New Nation

This manuscript has twenty-five mistakes! Some words are misspelled; others are the wrong word choice or date. Write the correct word or date above each underlined mistake.

              1800   p. 195
After he was elected president in <u>1796</u>, Thomas Jefferson faced many challenges. His inau-
                   Washington, D.C.   p. 195
guration in the muddy, unfinished capital of <u>New York City</u> indicated the work that lay ahead. He
           Federalist   p. 196   *five   p. 196*
tried to reverse many <u>Fedaralist</u> policies. For example, he restored the <u>two-year</u> residence require-
                      army   p. 196   *1801   p. 197*
ment for citizenship, he reduced the standing <u>militia</u>, and he repealed the Judiciary Act of <u>1789</u>.
                           Samuel Chase   p. 197
But the Senate refused to impeach the Federalist judge <u>John Pickering</u> and destroy the Supreme
                      National Bank   p. 197
Court's power. Jefferson himself left the successful <u>excise tax</u> intact.

                         Barbary   p. 197   *tribute   p. 197*
    His first foreign challenge came when pirates from the <u>Barbaric</u> States charged <u>embargo</u> fees
                  Tripolitan   p. 198
on ships that traded in the Mediterranean. The <u>Tripartisan</u> War, which started when Jefferson re-

fused to pay the fees, brought the United States Navy international respect. An even greater prob-
               Napoleon   p. 198
lem arose when the French ruler <u>LeClerc</u> sent a force to North America. Wishing to avoid war,
            Livingston   p. 198   *New Orleans   p. 198*
Jefferson sent ambassador Robert <u>Dearborn</u> to negotiate for the purchase of <u>St. Louis</u> and
                      Louisiana   p. 198   *$15 million   p. 198*
Florida. When the ambassador was offered the entire <u>Loisiana</u> Territory for only <u>$3 million</u>,
                         Constitution   p. 198
Jefferson agreed to purchase the land, even though he doubted that the <u>Bill of Rights</u> gave him
             Meriwether Lewis   p. 199
the power. He sent his private secretary, <u>William Clark</u>, to explore the new land. Zebulon Pike
                Mississippi   p. 202
went on another expedition to discover the source of the <u>Missouri</u> River.

    During his second term, Jefferson's main problem was America's neutral rights at sea. In
              Orders in Council   p. 202
1807 the British passed the <u>Milan Decree</u>, requiring American ships to stop in England.
             Berlin and Milan Decrees   p. 203
Meanwhile, France issued the <u>Orders in Council</u>, which allowed France to seize American ships
                      Chesapeake   p. 205
trading with Britain. When a British ship fired on the U.S.S. <u>*Chessapeek*</u>, Jefferson responded
 an embargo   p. 205
with a <u>blockade</u> to stop all exports to the warring countries. The new law aroused anger, espe-
      New England   p. 205
cially in <u>the West</u>, which was hurt by the loss of trade. Jefferson left his successor, President
James Madison   p. 206
<u>Henry Clay</u>, with a host of problems that eventually led to war.

American Republic

Case #2: Panic in the Midwest

Police departments across the Midwest are receiving reports of a herd of cattle on the loose. People have had their gardens trampled, their lawns eaten clean, and their noses terrorized by certain smells. The herd's favorite act of terrorism has been milk truck tipping late at night. The GIA has discovered that the herd is being led by udder-world boss Cow Capone. Last year Capone escaped from the maximum security pasture Cowcatraz. Recently Capone has tried to get more cows to join the herd by mailing out flyers to every farm in the Midwest. The flyers, written in MOO code, give clues to where the cows plan to head on their rampage. Police informant Jimmy the Bovine has translated the flyer. Now it's up to Sir Vey and you to track down the cows. Use the maps and text from Chapters 4 through 10 and the map of the Midwest (p. 217) to solve the clues.

3:00 P.M. Monday: The major city located in the Black Hills of the Midwest ___*Rapid City   p. 217*

8:00 P.M. Monday: The city where Moravian David Zeisberger faced trial as a spy ___*Detroit   p. 56*

11:00 A.M. Tuesday: The city at the western tip of Lake Superior ___*Duluth   p. 217*

5:00 P.M. Tuesday: The capital of the state in which these coordinates intersect: 45° N, 90° W

___*Madison   p. 217*

1:00 A.M. Wednesday: The place where George Rogers Clark captured a frontier outpost in

Illinois ___*Kaskaskia   p. 104*

9:00 A.M. Wednesday: The modern city located where Fort Dearborn once was ___*Chicago   p. 208*

4:00 P.M. Wednesday: The city near which the battle of Fallen Timbers was fought in 1794

___*Toledo   p. 175*

8:00 A.M. Thursday: The major city in Ohio located on the Ohio River ___*Cincinnati   p. 217*___

5:00 P.M. Thursday: The mountains in southern Missouri ___*Ozarks   p. 217*___

10:00 P.M. Thursday: The capital of the state where "Tornado Alley" ends in the North ___*Lincoln*   p. 216

6:00 A.M. Friday: The lake that Oliver Hazard Perry took control of in 1813 ___*Lake Erie   p. 210*___

10:00 A.M. Friday: The city found closest to the northern extent of Zebulon Pike's 1805 expedition ___*St. Cloud   p. 217*___

7:00 P.M. Friday: The city in South Dakota found on the river that Lewis and Clark explored ___*Pierre   p. 217*___

Saturday Rampage: The city located closest to the Door Peninsula ___*Green Bay   p. 217*___

9:00 A.M. Monday: The city located approximately three hundred miles east of Sioux City ___*Dubuque   p. 217*___

4:00 P.M. Monday: The state capital closest to the river named in the Treaty of Paris in 1783 ___*St. Paul   pp. 108, 217*___

2:00 A.M. Tuesday: The city in Kansas found in the Great Plains ___*Dodge City   p. 217*___

10:00 A.M. Tuesday: The city in Indiana located on the river that was the dividing line between slave and free states as determined by the Northwest Ordinance of 1787 ___*Evansville   pp. 117, 217*___

American Republic

Chapter 11   Activity A

Map Study: Missouri Compromise

Refer to the maps in the textbook on pages 221 and 224 to complete this map.

1. Label these territories: Michigan, Florida, Arkansas, Unorganized.

2. Label these new states: Indiana (1816), Mississippi (1817), Illinois (1818), Alabama (1819), Maine (1820), Missouri (1821).

3. With a colored pencil, draw the boundary between free and slave states as of 1820.

4. Place a star at the site of the Battle of Horseshoe Bend.

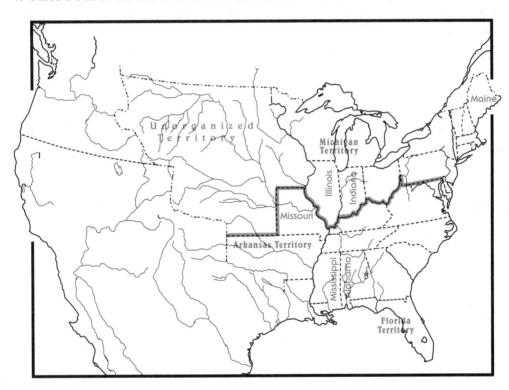

The Missouri Compromise

Answer these questions on the Missouri Compromise. (See the textbook and its maps on pages 646-47 and 224.)

1. What slave territory applied for statehood in 1819? _Missouri   p. 225_

2. What free territory applied for statehood in 1819? _Maine   p. 225_

3. What latitude became the northern boundary of slavery in the territories? _36°E 30'   p. 224_

4. Which five slave states were above this latitude? _Missouri, Kentucky, Virginia,_
   Maryland, Delaware   p. 224

5. Compare the number of states eventually created out of northern and southern territories. Did the North or the South eventually get more states from the territories? _The northern_
   territories eventually became at least eleven states; the southern territories became only three.   p. 224

American Republic

Chapter 11   Activity B

Comparing Presidential Campaigns

This era marked a major transition in American politics. Summarize each election, based on the information in your textbook. (Hint: Don't forget to read the boxes on each president.)

	Election of 1816	Election of 1820	Election of 1824	Election of 1828
Main Candidates	James Monroe Rufus King p. 219	James Monroe John Quincy Adams p. 220	Andrew Jackson John Quincy Adams William Crawford Henry Clay pp. 225-26	Andrew Jackson John Quincy Adams pp. 229-32
Main Parties	Democratic-Republican and Federalist	none (Democratic-Republican and Independent Republican)	Democratic-Republican (Republicans and state legislatures)	Democratic and National Republican
Style of Campaigning	Monroe–none; King–speeches	almost none	frequent speeches	mass campaigning (banners, barbecues, etc.); mudslinging
Voter Participation	little interest because of caucuses	little interest because of caucuses	increasing interest	widespread interest

1. What campaign marked the end of the Federalist Party? ___election of 1816   p. 220___

2. During what campaign did a candidate receive all but one electoral vote? ___election of 1820   p. 219___

3. The caucus system "died" in 1824. Why? ___Too many candidates were selected by state legislatures; in that election the candidate with national support lost.   p. 226___

4. During what campaign did the most popular candidate *lose*? ___election of 1824   p. 226___

5. What party was the predecessor of the Democratic Party? ___Democratic-Republican Party   p. 229___

6. Why did the number of voters double between 1824 and 1828? ___expansion of suffrage; new states   p. 229___

American Republic

Chapter 11   Activity C

Write Your Own Test: Matching   *Answers will vary.*

Write a phrase describing each name or term in the list. Then write the letter of the name or term in the blank.

A. John Quincy Adams   C. Henry Clay   E. James Monroe
B. John C. Calhoun   D. Andrew Jackson   F. Jose de San Martín

__A__ 1. *well-educated president; elected without a majority of the electoral vote   pp. 226-27*

__B__ 2. *South Carolina war hawk; Monroe's secretary of war; vice president under J. Q. Adams and Jackson*   pp. 220, 227, 229

__C__ 3. *Speaker of the House; deciding factor in J. Q. Adams's election; "corrupt bargain" for secretary of state*   p. 226

__D__ 4. *"Old Hickory"; hero of Horseshoe Bend; lost unfairly to J. Q. Adams in 1824; Democratic party leader*   pp. 226, 229

__E__ 5. *ushered in "Era of Good Feelings"; issued a new foreign policy   pp. 219, 223*

__F__ 6. *Creole revolutionary in South America   p. 222*

A. autocracy   C. incumbent   E. mudslinging
B. caucus   D. interstate commerce   F. tariff of abominations

__A__ 7. *government by one powerful ruler   p. 222*

__B__ 8. *a closed meeting of party leaders   p. 219*

__C__ 9. *a current officeholder who is running again   p. 219*

__D__ 10. *selling and transporting of goods from one state to another   p. 224*

__E__ 11. *making malicious statements about a political opponent   p. 229*

__F__ 12. *rise in import tax rates in 1828 that hurt southerners   pp. 227-28*

Write Your Own Test: Short Answer   *Answers will vary.*

Write a question for each of the answers below.

13. *What phrase describes James Monroe's two terms, which were relatively free from political clashes?   p. 219*   Era of Good Feelings

14. *What foreign policy, written by John Quincy Adams, became a foundational element of American foreign policy?   p. 223*   Monroe Doctrine

15. *In what case did Chief Justice John Marshall assert, "The power to tax includes the power to destroy"?   p. 224*   *McCulloch v. Maryland*

16. *What agreement, offered by Henry Clay, temporarily settled the political dispute over the balance between slave and free states? p. 225*   Missouri Compromise

17. *What party, headed by Andrew Jackson, was composed largely of former Democratic-Republicans?   p. 229*   Democratic Party

Write Your Own Test: Multiple Choice   *Answers will vary.*

Write four choices for each problem. Then write the letter of the correct choice in the blank.

D 18. Andrew Jackson was considered a hero for all these reasons *except* that

    A. __he won the battle of Horseshoe Bend.   p. 220__

    B. __he won the battle of New Orleans.   p. 226__

    C. __he invaded Florida and deposed the Spanish governor.   p. 221__

    D. __he killed Alexander Hamilton in a duel.   p. 231__

D 19. The Monroe Doctrine introduced all of these principles of foreign policy *except* that

    A. __European nations could not set up new colonies in America.   p. 223__

    B. __the U.S. would avoid European wars unless its rights were menaced.   p. 223__

    C. __the U.S. would consider any European intervention in America dangerous.   p. 223__

    D. __the U.S. would intervene in Latin American autocracies.__

C 20. The Missouri Compromise included all of these provisions *except* that

    A. __Missouri would come in as a slave state.   p. 225__

    B. __Maine would come in as a free state.   p. 225__

    C. __slavery would be forbidden in the new territories.__

    D. __slavery would be protected south of 36°E 30'.   p. 225__

D 21. During the election of 1824, the Democratic-Republican candidate was

    A. __John Quincy Adams.__

    B. __Henry Clay.__

    C. __Andrew Jackson.__

    D. __William Crawford.   p. 225__

D 22. John Quincy Adams was accused of making a "corrupt bargain" when he

    A. __signed the Missouri Compromise.__

    B. __agreed to support the "tariff of abominations."__

    C. __sent southern delegates to the Pan-American Conference.__

    D. __made Henry Clay the secretary of state.   p. 226__

D 23. The election of 1828 differed from most earlier campaigns for all of these reasons *except* that

    A. __techniques of mass campaigning appeared.   p. 229__

    B. __more voters participated in the election.   p. 229__

    C. __the mudslinging was some of the worst ever.   p. 229__

    D. __the candidates were selected by caucus.__

American Republic

Chapter 11   Activity D

Clustering

One way to study for a test is by *clustering*. To cluster, find the main topics in the chapter and then "cluster" about five or more main facts under each topic. In the exercise below, write the number of each fact in the blank beside the topic where it belongs.

A. James Monroe's Election *1, 2, 8, 11, 21* _____

B. James Monroe's Foreign Concerns *7, 10, 13, 14, 20, 22, 23* _____

C. James Monroe's Internal Concerns *4, 5, 15, 16, 24* _____

D. John Quincy Adams's Election and Concerns *3, 6, 9, 12, 17, 18, 19* _____

1. He refused to wage an active campaign for the presidency. *p. 219*

2. Political rivalries almost came to an end during his "Era of Good Feelings." *p. 219*

3. The Democratic Party arose in opposition to Henry Clay's system for improving the national economy. *pp. 227-29*

4. The practice of issuing bank notes not backed by gold or silver helped cause the Panic of '19. *p. 223*

5. The Missouri Compromise was a temporary measure that failed to settle the basic problem of slavery. *p. 225*

6. The South threatened to leave the Union over the "tariff of abominations." *p. 228*

7. Europeans threatened to intervene in the new, weak republics of Latin America. *p. 222*

8. A caucus selected Madison's secretary of state to be the next presidential candidate. *p. 219*

9. He was elected president after a supposed "corrupt bargain" with Henry Clay. *p. 226*

10. Andrew Jackson exceeded his orders when he invaded Florida and deposed the Spanish governor. *p. 221*

11. He said, "I want the best men in the country working with me regardless of their party beliefs." *p. 220*

12. Cold and aloof, he refused to award jobs to his followers. *p. 227*

13. He purchased Florida from Spain for $5 million. *p. 221*

14. He included the Monroe Doctrine in his annual address to Congress, warning Europeans not to meddle in the Western Hemisphere. *p. 223*

15. In *McCulloch v. Maryland,* John Marshall ruled that the federal government could not be taxed by the states. *p. 224*

16. The Supreme Court gave the federal government power to regulate interstate commerce. *p. 224*

17. His reelection campaign involved some of America's worst mudslinging. *p. 229*

18. Simón Bolívar's Pan-American Conference was never attended by U.S. delegates. *pp. 228-29*

19. He was elected president even though Andrew Jackson received more popular votes. *p. 226*

20. Russia built a fort a short distance north of San Francisco. *p. 222*

21. He agreed to run for president on the condition that he would not be tied to a single political party. *p. 219*

22. Runaway slaves and Indians were using Florida as a haven to avoid capture. *p. 221*

23. Great Britain became the first European nation to cooperate with the new republics in Latin America. *p. 222*

24. Tallmadge's controversial amendment banned the movement of slaves into Missouri. *p. 225*

Skill: Synthesis

American Republic

Sentence Outlining

For each heading in Chapter 12, write a short, complete sentence. (An outline made up of sentences is called a sentence outline.) *Answers will vary.*

A. Jacksonian Democracy was advantageous for some.

    1. Jackson introduced the spoils system.

    2. _Jackson consulted a "kitchen cabinet."   p. 236_

    3. _Jackson mistreated the Indians.   p. 236_

        a. Jackson's harsh policies reflected common attitudes.

        b. _Jackson reacted to trouble in Georgia by forcibly removing the Cherokees.   p. 237_

        c. _The Black Hawk War started when starving Indians tried to return to their lands.   p. 238_

B. The nullification controversy arose during the Jackson presidency.

    1. _Tariff troubles arose because sections of the country disagreed on the purpose of tariffs.   p. 239_

        a. The reasons for tariffs were to raise money and to protect infant industry.

        b. _The "tariff of abominations" angered southerners, who feared higher prices.   p. 240_

    2. _John C. Calhoun became the defender of states' rights.   p. 240_

    3. _Webster debated Hayne on the issue of nullification.   pp. 240-41_

    4. _Calhoun and Jackson clashed over states' rights.   p. 241_

    5. _A time of crisis arose when South Carolina threatened to secede.   pp. 241-42_

    6. _The Compromise Tariff of 1833 avoided violence.   p. 242_

C. _Jackson's veto of the National Bank was the main issue in the election of 1832.   pp. 243-44_

    1. _Banker Nicholas Biddle, head of the National Bank, was a threat to state banks.   p. 243_

    2. _Henry Clay made the recharter of the National Bank the issue in the election of 1832.   p. 244_

    3. _Jackson placed government money in state "pet banks."   p. 244_

    4. _Jackson issued a Specie Circular to stop inflation.   p. 245_

D. _The effects of the Jackson administration were extensive—some good and some bad.   p. 245_

    1. _In the election of 1836, Jackson's hand-picked choice defeated the Whigs.   p. 246_

    2. _The Van Buren years were marred by economic depression.   p. 247_

    3. _William Henry Harrison was elected the first Whig president in 1840.   p. 247_

    4. _"Tyler Too" unexpectedly became president when Harrison died.   p. 248_

        a. _Tyler's opposition to the Whigs made him "a man without a party."   pp. 248-49_

        b. _The Webster-Ashburton Treaty settled the Maine boundary dispute.   p. 249_

        c. _At the end of Tyler's term, Americans were clamoring for a strong leader.   p. 250_

American Republic

Alexis de Tocqueville's *Democracy in America*

Democracy in America was written by a brilliant Frenchman named Alexis de Tocqueville, who visited America in 1831 during the pivotal administration of Andrew Jackson. Read this selection from the chapter "Tyranny of the Majority" and answer the questions that follow.

In my opinion the main evil of the present democratic institutions of the United States does not arise, as is often asserted in Europe, from their weakness, but from their overpowering strength. I am not so much alarmed at the excessive liberty which reigns in that country, as at the inadequate guarantees against tyranny.

When an individual or a party is wronged in the United States, to whom can he turn for redress? To public opinion? Public opinion forms the majority. To the legislature? It represents the majority and implicitly obeys its instructions. To the executive power? It is appointed by the majority and is a passive tool in its hands. The public troops consist of the majority under arms. The jury is the majority invested with the right of hearing judicial cases. And in certain states even the judges are elected by the majority. However iniquitous or absurd the evil of which you complain may be, you must submit to it as well as you can.

A striking example of the excesses to which the despotism of the majority may lead occurred at Baltimore in the year 1812. At that time the war

was very popular in Baltimore. A newspaper that had taken the other side of the question aroused the indignation of the inhabitants. The people assembled, broke the printing presses, and attacked the houses of the editors. The militia was called out, but no one obeyed the call. The only means of saving the poor wretches who were threatened by the frenzy of the mob was to throw them into prison as common criminals. But even this precaution was ineffective. The mob collected again during the night, the magistrates again made a vain attempt to call out the militia, the prison was forced open, one of the editors was killed on the spot, and the others were left for dead. The guilty parties were acquitted by the jury when they were brought to trial. . . .

I do not say that acts of tyranny frequently occur in America at the present day. But I do say that no solid barrier exists against them. The causes that limit the government are to be found in the circumstances and customs of the country more than its laws.

1. What did de Tocqueville find most alarming about democracy in America? ___the shortage of "guarantees against tyranny"___

2. If the majority does something evil that hurts you, what is your only option?___"submit . . . as well as you can"___

3. Why did the people who attacked the editors go free?___The jury acquitted them.___

4. What do you think de Tocqueville meant by the "tyranny of the majority"?___the ability of the majority to force a minority to submit___

5. If an anti-Christian majority elects people who hate Christians to the legislature, presidency, and judiciary, do we have any guarantees against tyranny?___not really; Christians need to pray to God for peace. It is unwise to trust in a form of government.___

Skill: Original Sources

American Republic

Nullification Crisis

Why didn't the nullification crisis end in civil war? Complete the chart by writing down the causes of northern actions and the southern reactions. The answers are listed at the bottom. (You will see in Chapter 16 how a different order of events caused the Civil War in 1861.)

Cause	Northern Action	Southern Reaction
Federalists want to stay in power.	Alien and Sedition Acts (1798)	*The Virginia and Kentucky Resolutions first assert the right of nullification.*
Northerners want protective tariffs. **p. 240**	"Tariff of Abominations" (1828)	**Fearing for the South's economy, Calhoun first asserts nullification.** **p. 240**
Southerners bargain with the West for a lower tariff. p. 240	Webster-Hayne debate (1830)	**Calhoun resigns vice-presidency to lead the fight for states' rights. p. 241**
Northerners offer a slightly revised protective tariff. p. 241	Tariff of 1832	**Nullifiers give up hope for a revenue tariff. p. 241**
S.C. passes the Ordinance of Nullification. pp. 241-42	Force Bill (1833)	**S.C. calls a national convention to support nullification. p. 242**
S.C. fails to receive support for nullification. p. 242	Compromise of 1833	**S.C. withdraws nullification of the tariff. p. 242**
S.C. holds only the Force Bill nullified. p. 242	no further action	**Question of states' rights remains unsettled. p. 242**

Causes
S.C. holds only the Force Bill nullified.
S.C. passes the Ordinance of Nullification.
Northerners want protective tariffs.
Northerners offer a slightly revised protective tariff.
S.C. fails to receive support for nullification.
Southerners bargain with the West for a lower tariff.

Southern Reactions
S.C. withdraws nullification of the tariff.
Nullifiers give up hope for a revenue tariff.
Question of states' rights remains unsettled.
S.C. calls a national convention to support nullification.
Calhoun resigns vice-presidency to lead the fight for states' rights.
Fearing for the South's economy, Calhoun first asserts nullification.

American Republic

Political Cartoons

Although political cartoons existed in colonial days, they began to take their modern form during the Jacksonian era. Political cartoons appeal to the common people. "A picture is worth a thousand words," the saying goes. Look at these two political cartoons from newspapers of the period and then answer the questions that follow.

A.

Tariff of Abominations (1832)

B.

Van Buren's Reelection Campaign (1840)

Cartoon A

1. Which direction is the wind blowing? _south_____

2. What two burdens are on the southerner's back? _tariffs and taxes_____

3. List three differences between the North and the South. (Hint: *To let* means "for rent.")

   thin versus fat man, plain versus fancy clothes, empty building and docked ships

   _versus activity at building and empty harbor_____

4. What link joins the two main figures? _Union_____

5. Did the cartoonist support the North or the South? _South_____

Cartoon B

6. What two things block Van Buren's road to the White House? _hard cider and log cabins_

7. Who is pulling Van Buren on his journey to the White House? _Andrew Jackson_

8. What burden on Van Buren's back makes his trip difficult? _sub-treasury system_

9. What alternative does Van Buren have to his trip to the White House? _home (Kinderhook)_

10. Was the cartoonist for or against Van Buren's reelection? _against reelection_

American Republic

Chapter 12   Activity E

Presidents of the Jacksonian Era

Match the presidents with the phrases that are associated with them.

A. Andrew Jackson   C. William Henry Harrison
B. Martin Van Buren   D. John Tyler

_D_ 1. "a man without a party" *p. 249*

_A_ 2. the Hermitage in Tennessee *p. 234*

_D_ 3. annexation of Texas *p. 250*

_C_ 4. longest inaugural address *p. 248*

_A_ 5. Battle of New Orleans *p. 234*

_D_ 6. Webster-Ashburton Treaty *p. 249*

_A_ 7. Black Hawk War *p. 238*

_B_ 8. independent treasury *p. 247*

_B_ 9. appointment of Chief Justice Roger B. Taney *p. 247*

_A_ 10. Specie Circular *p. 245*

_A_ 11. "pet banks" *p. 244*

_D_ 12. "his accidency" *p. 249*

_A_ 13. "spoils system" *p. 236*

_D_ 14. running mate of old Tippecanoe *p. 247*

_B_ 15. "Old Kinderhook" (O.K.) *p. 246*

_A_ 16. forcible removal of the Cherokees from Georgia *p. 237*

_A_ 17. "Kitchen Cabinet" *p. 236*

_D_ 18. land act giving squatters the right to buy land *p. 248*

_A_ 19. Force Bill *p. 242*

_D_ 20. resignation of his entire cabinet *p. 249*

_A_ 21. vetoed the recharter of the National Bank *p. 244*

_A_ 22. Compromise Tariff of 1833 *p. 242*

_C_ 23. died after only one month in office *p. 248*

_A_ 24. *Worcester v. Georgia* *p. 237*

_B_ 25. plagued by an economic depression *p. 247*

_A_ 26. nullification crisis *pp. 241-42*

_A_ 27. self-taught; champion of the "common man" *pp. 234-35*

_C_ 28. first Whig president *p. 247*

_B_ 29. first president not born a British citizen *p. 247*

_C_ 30. first president to die in office *p. 248*

_A_ 31. first president born in a log cabin *p. 235*

_B_ 32. the hand-picked successor of Andrew Jackson *p. 246*

_A_ 33. rich planter from Tennessee *p. 235*

_A_ 34. "Our Federal Union: it must and shall be preserved!" *p. 241*

_B_ 35. "The less government interferes with private pursuits, the better for the general prosperity." *p. 247*

American Republic

Modified True/False

If the statement is true, write the word *true* in the blank. If it is false, change the under-lined words to make the statement true.

<u>first p. 234</u>	1. Andrew Jackson was the <u>second</u> president born west of the original thirteen colonies.
<u>true p. 237</u>	2. Andrew Jackson <u>ignored</u> John Marshall's order in *Worcester v. Georgia.*
<u>"spoils system" p. 236</u>	3. The "<u>kitchen cabinet</u>" was Jackson's method of handing out government jobs to loyal followers.
<u>Sequoyah p. 238</u>	4. <u>Black Hawk</u> was a Cherokee scholar who developed an alphabet for his people.
<u>true p. 237</u>	5. The <u>Cherokees</u> fought on Jackson's side at the battle of Horseshoe Bend.
<u>protective p. 239</u>	6. A <u>revenue</u> tariff is designed to protect infant industries from foreign competition.
<u>southern p. 239</u>	7. Protective tariffs were unpopular among the <u>northern</u> states.
<u>true p. 239</u>	8. Most money in the South was invested in slaves and <u>cotton</u>.
<u>nullification p. 240</u>	9. John C. Calhoun offered the theory of <u>secession</u> to protect South Carolina from harmful federal tariffs.
<u>Daniel Webster p. 241</u>	10. <u>Robert Y. Hayne</u> declared, "Liberty and Union, now and forever, one and inseparable!"
<u>true p. 241</u>	11. Calhoun resigned from the <u>vice-presidency</u> to lead the fight for states' rights.
<u>true p. 242</u>	12. The Compromise of 1833 gradually <u>lowered</u> tariffs to twenty percent.
<u>the National Bank p. 243</u>	13. Jackson's reelection campaign focused on the future of <u>states' rights</u>.
<u>Specie Circular p. 245</u>	14. The <u>Force Bill</u> required anyone who bought government lands to pay for them in specie.
<u>true p. 246</u>	15. The Whig party ran <u>three</u> presidential candidates in the election of 1836.
<u>Democratic p. 247</u>	16. Van Buren had the opportunity to change control of the Supreme Court to the <u>Whig</u> Party.
<u>squatters p. 248</u>	17. Settlers on western lands without titles to the land are called <u>lame ducks</u>.
<u>true p. 249</u>	18. <u>Daniel Webster</u> negotiated a settlement of the boundary between Maine and Canada.

Skill: Comprehension

American Republic

Chapter 13   Activity A

Map Study: Growth of Transportation

Refer to maps in the text on pages 255, 261, and 264 to complete the map on the next page.

1. Label these lakes: Michigan, Erie.

2. Label these towns and cities: Portland; Boston; Baltimore; Washington, D.C.; New York City; Philadelphia; Buffalo; Albany; Pittsburgh; Wheeling; Cleveland; Vandalia; Chicago; Boonesboro; St. Louis; Savannah; Augusta; Atlanta; New Orleans.

3. Using a blue pencil, draw and label these roads: Boston Post Road, Great Wagon Road, Wilderness Road, National Road.

4. Using a green pencil, draw these canals: Erie, Illinois and Michigan, Ohio and Erie.

5. Using a red pencil, draw these railroad routes:

   • the main route on the East Coast from Portland to Savannah
   • the main route in the West from New Orleans to Chicago
   • the main route connecting Baltimore and St. Louis
   • the main route connecting St. Louis, Chicago, Cleveland, Philadelphia, and New York City

Map Questions

Answer these questions based on the textbook and its maps on pages 255, 261, and 264.

1. What Indian path became a wagon road through the Appalachians? _Great Warrior's Path p. 256_

2. What pioneer road aided the settlement of Kentucky? _Wilderness Road   p. 257_

3. What federally funded road aided settlement of the Northwest? _National (Cumberland) Road   p. 257_

4. How were turnpikes paid for? _Private companies built the roads and charged tolls. p. 258_

5. What was the main purpose of a "post road"? _It was necessary for the delivery of mail. p. 265_

6. What natural pass did Daniel Boone use through the Appalachians? _Cumberland Gap   p. 257_

7. Name a city that was both a steamboat *and* a railroad center. _Answers will vary.   pp. 261, 264_

8. Why did New York City grow as a result of the Erie Canal? _Traffic had to pass through New York City to reach Albany, where the canal began.   pp. 259-60_

9. What Maryland city became a major railroad center with many branches? _Baltimore   p. 264 (map)_

10. What were the first two cities linked by telegraph? _Baltimore and Washington, D.C.   p. 266_

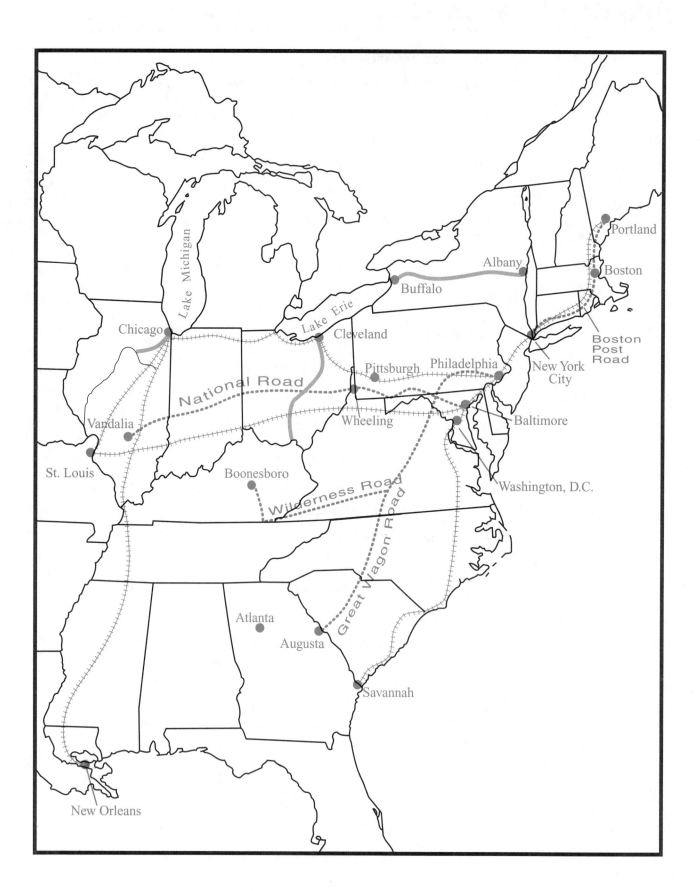

American Republic

Chapter 13   Activity B

Improvements in Transportation and Communication

Transportation and communication improved dramatically during the 1800s. For each improvement, write the name of the man behind its first success, the date of its success, one advantage, and one disadvantage. Then answer the questions on the back.

<table>
<tr><th></th><th>Improvement</th><th>Supporter</th><th>Date</th><th>Advantage</th><th>Disadvantage</th></tr>
<tr><td rowspan="4">Overland Transportation</td><td>stagecoach
p. 255</td><td></td><td>1766</td><td>increased speed with more horses</td><td>dependence on good weather;
need for good roads</td></tr>
<tr><td>plank road
p. 257</td><td></td><td>1845</td><td>smooth surface</td><td>expensive to build and maintain</td></tr>
<tr><td>macadamized road
p. 257</td><td></td><td>1858</td><td>cheap stones;
good drainage;
easy maintenance</td><td>difficulty of crushing stones and digging road beds</td></tr>
<tr><td>locomotive
pp. 262-63, 265</td><td>Peter Cooper
(Tom Thumb)</td><td>1830</td><td>fast and cheap;
not affected by weather;
not dependent on water</td><td>not useful for local travel</td></tr>
<tr><td rowspan="4">Water Transportation</td><td>flatboat
p. 258</td><td></td><td></td><td>floating downstream in shallow water</td><td>high rates;
difficulty moving upstream</td></tr>
<tr><td>steamboat
pp. 258-60</td><td>Robert Fulton
(Clermont)</td><td>1807</td><td>paddling upstream;
opening of the West</td><td>limited to water</td></tr>
<tr><td>canal
pp. 260-63</td><td>DeWitt Clinton
(Erie Canal)</td><td>1817</td><td>opening of new water routes</td><td>expensive to build and maintain;
closed during the winter;
practical only in flat areas</td></tr>
<tr><td>clipper
(see textbook pp. 279-80)</td><td>Donald McKay
(Flying Cloud)</td><td>1850</td><td>increased speed</td><td>need for experienced crews;
dependence on wind</td></tr>
<tr><td rowspan="3">Communications</td><td>post roads
p. 265</td><td></td><td></td><td>rapid movement of letters between major cities</td><td>cost of building good roads</td></tr>
<tr><td>pony express
p. 265</td><td></td><td>1860</td><td>rapid movement of letters from the East to California</td><td>need for many horses, stations, and riders</td></tr>
<tr><td>telegraph
p. 266</td><td>Samuel F. B. Morse</td><td>1844</td><td>instant relay of information;
scheduling of railroads</td><td>need for a complex network;
inconvenient for private communication</td></tr>
</table>

Thought Questions

Answer these questions based on the textbook and the chart on the previous page.

1. What is the difference between transportation and communication? (Consult a dictionary.)

   Transportation is a means of moving people or things. Communication is a means of

   sending messages.

2. Why do you think Americans continued to build roads after the locomotive was invented?

   Roads are more efficient when you travel to nearby places or to remote regions. Building

   railroads took many years, and railroads were practical only on major routes.

3. Railroads eventually took the place of canals because railroads were so much cheaper. Why do you think the canal craze continued until 1850, twenty years *after* Peter Cooper proved the value of railroads in 1830?

   Laying tracks and constructing locomotives took time. Many people were slow to see

   the potential of railroads.

4. The federal government stopped construction of the National Road in the late 1830s before it reached St. Louis.

   - Where did it stop? *Vandalia, Illinois   p. 257*

   - What changes in transportation during the 1830s and 1840s made the road less practical?

   canals and locomotives   pp. 261, 263

5. Macadamized roads are still being built today. Why do you think this type of road construction became more popular than the smooth plank roads?

   Macadamized roads were easier to build and maintain. Crushed stones are easier to

   produce than wood planks, and they last longer.   p. 257

6. Why do you think telegraph poles were placed alongside railroad tracks? *The railroad*

   tracks already connected the major cities, and the paths had already been cleared.

   Also, the railroads used the telegraph to maintain their schedules.   p. 266

7. Some improvements in transportation and communication refined old sources of power, such as wind, water, and horses. Other improvements adapted new sources of power, such as steam and electricity. In each example below, give one reason you think the new source of power proved more successful than the old source.

   - locomotive over stagecoach *greater endurance; cheaper to fuel; faster*

   - steamboat over clipper *not dependent on wind; less need for a skilled crew; larger capacity*

   - telegraph over pony express *faster; less expensive to maintain*

8. How did improvements in transportation benefit communication? *Communication of*

   messages often requires some means of transportation. The postal service could move

   mail more rapidly by improved roads, steamship, and rail.

American Republic

Chapter 13   Activity C

Line Graphs: American Growth (1790-1860)

Draw line graphs from the information provided.

Population Growth (in millions): Plot the population figures on the graph and connect them.

Year	1790	1800	1810	1820	1830	1840	1850	1860
Population	4	5	7	10	13	17	23	31

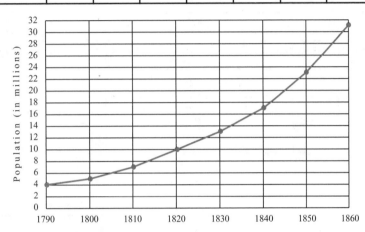

Growth of Transportation (in thousands of miles): Use three colored pencils to plot mileage.

	1790	1800	1810	1820	1830	1840	1850	1860
Turnpikes	0	1	2	3	3	3	2	1
Canals	0	0	0	0	1	2	3	3
Railroads	0	0	0	0	0	3	9	31

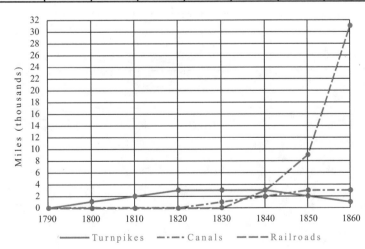

Growth of Cities

You can use line graphs to show both the total number of cities in America and how many cities are in each size group. You will need four colored pencils. First plot the numbers for cities with a population between 25,000 and 50,000, and then color in the space below your line. Next add to these figures the number of cities with a population between 50,000 and 100,000. Plot this *total,* and then color the blank space below the line with the second color. Do the same thing for cities between 100,000 and 250,000 and cities above 250,000.

	1790	1800	1810	1820	1830	1840	1850	1860
250,000+	0	0	0	0	0	1	1	3
100,000-250,000	0	0	0	1	1	2	5	6
50,000-100,000	0	1	2	2	3	2	4	7
25,000-50,000	2	2	2	2	3	7	16	19
Total	2	3	4	5	7	12	26	35

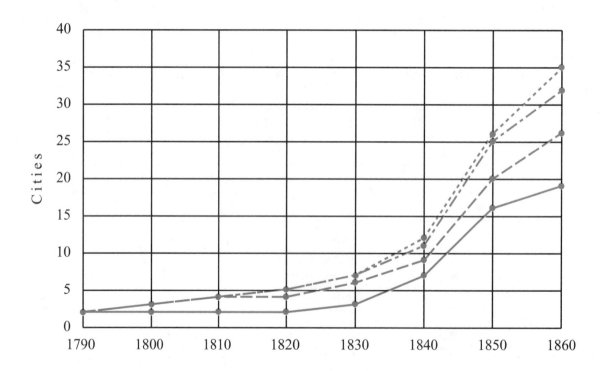

American Republic

Chapter 13   Activity D

The Costs of Westward Expansion   ☆ *Classroom discussion*

Here are some practical math questions that American businessmen and governments had to answer in the pre-Civil War era. You may use a calculator to solve them.

1. A farmer in Illinois wants to send a ton of wheat to New York City. The wheat must travel 125 miles by steamboat up the Illinois River to La Salle, 100 miles by flatboat on the newly completed Illinois and Michigan Canal to Chicago, 977 miles by sailboat to Buffalo, 363 miles by flatboat on the Erie Canal to Albany, and 150 miles by barge down the Hudson River to New York City. How many miles will his wheat travel?   *1,715 miles*

2. The National Road from Baltimore to Cumberland will be 130 miles long and cost $13,000 per mile. How much money must Congress spend?   *$1,690,000*

3. Donald McKay wants his clipper ship *Flying Cloud* to run from New York to San Francisco in a record 90 days. If the distance is 15,000 miles, how many miles must he travel each day?   *167 miles*

4. It costs $160 to take a flatboat down the Mississippi. If the boat charges 8¢ per pound of goods, how many pounds must it carry to break even?   *2,000 pounds*

5. New York's Erie Canal will stretch 363 miles around the north of the Allegheny Mountains from Albany to Buffalo. It will cost $20,000 per mile to build.

   • How much will the canal cost? *(Multiply miles by cost per mile.)*   *$7,260,000*

   • If boats travel at 3 miles per hour, how long will the trip take? *(Divide total miles by rate per hour.)*   *121 hours*

   • If boats with sleeping quarters charge passengers 5¢ per mile, how much will passengers pay for a trip from Albany to Buffalo? *(Multiply total miles by $0.05 per mile.)*   *$18.15*

6. Pennsylvania wants to build a 394-mile canal around the south of the Allegheny Mountains from Philadelphia to Pittsburgh. But the route is much hillier than New York's Erie Canal to the north of the Alleghenies. It will cost $30,000 per mile to build.

   • How much will the canal cost?   *$11,820,000*

   • Because the canal has many locks and a horse-drawn railroad in the middle, boats can travel at only 1.3 miles per hour. How long will the trip take?   *303 hours*

   • Because the canal is twice as expensive as the Erie Canal to operate, passengers pay 10¢ per mile. How much will passengers pay for a trip from Philadelphia to Pittsburgh?   *$39.40*

7. The world's longest railroad is the 136-mile run in South Carolina from Charleston to Hamburg. The *Best Friend* locomotive can travel at 17 miles per hour.

   • How long does the trip take? _8 hours_

   • If the track cost $5,600 per mile to lay, how much was its total cost? _$761,600_

8. John Fitch has built a steamboat for $15,000 to sail on the Delaware River between Philadelphia and Burlington. It travels the 20 miles in about 2.5 hours.

   • How fast does the steamboat travel? *(Divide miles by hours.)* _8 miles/hour_

   • If Fitch charged $1.50 per passenger and carried 1,050 passengers before the steamboat wrecked in a storm, how much money did he earn from passengers? _$1,575_

   • How much money did he lose? *(Subtract earnings from original investment.)* _$13,425_

9. Robert Fulton has built the *Clermont* for $20,000 to sail the Hudson River. The *Clermont* travels the 150 miles between New York City and Albany in about 30 hours.

   • How fast does the steamboat travel? _5 miles/hour_

   • If Fulton charged $5.50 per passenger and carried 6,546 passengers his first year, how much money did he earn from passengers? _$36,003_

   • How much money did he earn above his original investment? _$16,003_

10. You want to start a pony express to carry letters between St. Joseph, Missouri, and Sacramento, California. Even though the distance is 2,025 miles, you want mail to reach its destination in only 10 days.

   • How many miles must the ponies cover each day? _202.5 miles_

   • If you want a relay station every 15 miles, how many stations will you need? _135_

   • If each rider travels 75 miles, how many riders will carry each packet of mail? _27 riders_

11. F. B. Morse wants to build the first telegraph line to reach the 40 miles between Washington, D.C., and Baltimore. It will cost about $750 per mile.

   • How much should he request from Congress to build the line? _$30,000_

   • At this same rate, how much will a telegraph line running parallel to the pony express (2,025 miles) cost? _$1,518,750_

12. Brain Teaser: A land speculator purchased 20,000,000 acres in Kentucky and Virginia from the Cherokees for $44,500. The speculator pays Daniel Boone and 30 other men $2 a day to build the Wilderness Road, which takes 90 days to complete. It is 200 miles long, and the land around Boonesboro will sell for $4 per acre.

   • How much does each acre cost the land speculator? _0.2¢_

   • How much money does the speculator spend to build the road? _$5,580_

   • How much does each mile of road cost? _$27.90_

   • How many acres will the speculator need to sell to cover *all* his expenses? _12,520 acres_

Skill: Application

American Republic

Chapter 14   Activity A

American Inventions   ☆ *Classroom discussion*

American life changed dramatically during the 1800s as a result of inventions and improvements in agriculture and industry. For each invention or improvement below, write who introduced it, how it worked, and what impact it had on American society.

Invention	Inventor	Function of Invention	Impact of Invention on Society
steel plow *pp. 270-71*	*John Deere*	*cutting of smooth, straight furrows without the soil sticking to the plow blades*	*more grain planted with less work; opening and conquering of western prairies*
horse-drawn reaper *p. 271*	*Cyrus McCormick*	*cutting or harvesting of grain by machine*	*more grain harvested with less work; greater profits for farmers; increased exports of grain; less need for farm workers*
cotton gin *pp. 271-72*	*Eli Whitney*	*quick cleaning of short-staple cotton*	*increased profits in growing cotton; increased exports of cotton; increased dependence on slavery in the South*
American textile factory system *pp. 273-75*	*Samuel Slater*	*the collecting of workers into one place with set schedules and division of labor*	*more work done outside the home; less need for skilled workers; growth of child labor; cheaper yarn for clothes*
hand-cranked sewing machine *p. 275*	*Elias Howe (Walter Hunt)*	*rapid sewing of yarn into clothing by machine*	*less time needed to sew garments; increase of textile factories*
foot-treadle sewing machine *p. 275*	*Isaac Singer*	*rapid sewing that leaves the operator's hands free; curved seams*	*same as above; first patent pool in America; first million-dollar-per-year advertising; installment or time-payment plans*
interchangeable parts *p. 276*	*Eli Whitney*	*assembly of guns from identical pieces that are made with molds*	*less need for skilled workers; mass production of guns and other products*
clipper ships *p. 279*	*John W. Griffiths (Donald McKay)*	*sharp point on the bow; numerous sails*	*increased speeds of sea traders; rapid movement of gold seekers going west*

Reinforcement: Sections 1-3   Skill: Charts   **81**

American Republic

Interpreting Pictures

You can learn a lot from historical pictures if you study them carefully. Look at the picture in the textbook on page 273. Then answer the questions below.

Scene in the Hold of the "Blood-Stained Gloria" (from the Library of Congress)

1. What are the only two sources of light in the hold? _lantern and skylight_

2. What do the white men have in their hands? _lantern, rifle, sword_

3. What differences in clothes do you see between the white men and the slaves?
   The white men are fully dressed and fashionable with jackets and hats. The
   slaves are chained and almost naked.

4. What signs do you see that the slaves are being treated harshly?
   chains, whip, darkness, overcrowding, small barrel of water, fainting slave

5. What evidence do you see that the hold is too crowded?
   The slaves must sit up and pull up their knees. The white men barely have room
   to stand.

6. How would you describe the looks in the slaves' eyes?
   Answers will vary. (terrified, despairing)

7. Did the artist support the slave trade? _no_

American Republic

Rev. Henry A. Miles on *Lowell, As It Was and As It Is*

In 1846 Rev. Henry Miles published a detailed history of Lowell, Massachusetts (an early mill town for girls). He said the only purpose of his book was a "careful presentation of the facts." Answer the questions about his "facts" in each excerpt.

The superintendent, from his room, has the whole of the corporation under his eye. On the one side are the boarding-houses, all of which are under his care, and are rented only to known and approved tenants. On the other side are the mills, in each room of which he has stationed some carefully selected overseer, who is held responsible for the work, good order, and proper management of his room. . . . The superintendent's mind regulates all; his plans, matured and decided by the directors of the company, who visit him every week, control all. He presides over one of the most perfect systems of subdivided and yet well-defined responsibility. . . .

1. Who supervises the girls' "good order" in the mill rooms? __*overseer*__

Each of the long blocks of boarding-houses is divided into six or eight tenements, and are generally three stories high. These tenements are finished off in a style much above the common farmhouses of the country. . . . These are constantly kept clean, the buildings well painted, and the premises thoroughly whitewashed every spring, at the corporation's expense. The front room is usually the common eating-room of the house, and the kitchen is in the rear. The keeper of the house, (commonly a widow, with her family of children,) has her parlor in some part of the establishment, and in some houses there is a sitting-room for the use of the boarders.

The remainder of the apartments are sleeping-rooms. In each of these are lodged two, four, and in some cases six boarders; and the room has an air of neatness and comfort, exceeding what most of the occupants have been accustomed to in their paternal homes. In many cases, these rooms are not sufficiently large for the number who occupy them; and oftentimes that attention is not paid to their ventilation which a due regard to health demands. These are points upon which a reform is called for. . . . At the same time, it should in justice be added, that the evil alluded to is not peculiar to Lowell, and will not probably appear to be a crying one, if the case should be brought into comparison with many [other] apartments. . . .

Regulations to be observed by persons occupying the boarding-houses:
- No disorderly or improper conduct must be allowed in the houses.
- The doors must be closed at 10 o'clock in the evening.
- Those who keep the houses, when required, must give an account of their boarders with regard to their general conduct, and whether they are in the habit of attending public worship.

2. Who supervises the girls' "general conduct" in the boarding houses? __*keeper of the house*__

3. What health problem is described in this excerpt? __*overcrowding and poor ventilation*__

   What fact does Miles use to excuse this problem? __*The apartments are no worse*__

   __*than elsewhere.*__

[The time allowed for meals] is too short for a due regard to health. . . . And yet it is probably as long as most business men allow to themselves; it is probably as long as is spent at the tables of more than half of our public hotels. For the sake of the operatives we wish that the time for meals was lengthened, but we do not see the propriety of calling for reform in those habits of hasty eating which pervade the whole country, and characterize our nation. . . .

4. What health problem is described in this excerpt? _____*hasty eating of meals*_____

What facts does Miles use to excuse this problem? _____*The practice is common to*_____

_____*businessmen and in hotels. Indeed, the practice is characteristic of Americans.*_____

_____

No fact connected with the manufacturing business, has been so often, or so strongly objected to as this, that the average daily time of running the mills is twelve hours and ten minutes. It is no part the object of this book to defend any thing which may be shown to be wrong, its sole purpose being a careful presentation of the facts. Arguments are not needed to prove that toil, if it be continued for this length of time, each day, month after month, and year after year, is excessive and too much for the tender frames of young women to bear. No one can more sincerely desire, than the writer of this book, that they had more leisure time for mental improvement and social enjoyment. It must be remembered, however, that their work is comparatively light. All the hard processes, not conducted by men, are performed by machines, the movements of which female operatives are required merely to oversee and adjust. . . .

The average number of hours in which they are actually employed is not more than ten and a half. They are out to go shopping, to repair their clothes, to take care of themselves in any occasional illness, to see friends visiting the city, to call on sick friends here; nor are reasonable requests of this kind refused. Many of these girls, moreover, in the course of each year, take a vacation of a few weeks, to return to their homes. In these absences the work of the mill is not suspended. The wheels continue their revolutions for the prescribed number of hours. The processes are temporarily super-intended by other hands. To suppose that every operative is on duty just as long as the machinery is in motion, is an error of the most deceptive kind.

5. What is the most common objection to the manufacturing? _____*long hours*_____

What facts does Miles use to excuse this problem? _____*The work is comparatively light.*_____

_____*The girls receive time off and vacations. The average number of hours is only ten and*_____

_____*one half.*_____

Why does Miles call this objection "an error of the most deceptive kind"? _____*The*_____

_____*objection does not account for all the "facts."*_____

6. Do you think the girls' lives were worse at the boarding houses than on the farm? _____

Support your opinion from these excerpts. _____*Answers will vary. (Miles seems to*_____

_____*think that conditions were better in the factory.)*_____

Skill: Original Sources

American Republic

Map Study: Expanding Sea Trade

You may want to review basic geographic terms before you assign this activity.

Use a world map or globe to help you answer these questions about America's expanding trade (text pp. 278-79).

Opening a Three-Corner Trade Route with China

1. Check the geographic features that Samuel Shaw's ginseng-filled *Empress of China* would have crossed on its voyage from New York to China.

   ☑ 0° latitude (equator)   ❑ 150°W longitude   ☑ Tropic of Cancer
   ☑ 0° longitude (prime meridian) ❑ 60°N latitude   ☑ Tropic of Capricorn

2. Check the geographic features that Robert Gray's trinket-laden *Columbia* would have crossed on its voyage from Massachusetts to Oregon.

   ☑ 0° latitude (equator)   ❑ 150°W longitude   ☑ Tropic of Cancer
   ❑ 0° longitude (prime meridian) ❑ 60°N latitude   ☑ Tropic of Capricorn

3. Check the latitudes that Gray's ship sailed during his trip from Oregon to China.

   ☑ 0° to 45°N   ❑ 0° to 45°S   ❑ 45°N to 90°N

4. On his trip around the world, which geographic lines did Gray cross?

   ❑ all lines of latitude   ☑ all lines of longitude

5. Which direction did the "lords of the China trade" sail on their three-corner trade route?

   ☑ westward   ❑ eastward

6. If you flew an airplane straight to each stop, approximately how many degrees of longitude would you cross each time? (Hint: Your estimates should add up to 360°.)

   • East Coast to Pacific Coast ___45°-50°___

   • Pacific Coast to China ___105°-130°___

   • China to East Coast ___190°-215°___

Adding New Markets

7. Find Brazil and the western islands of Indonesia (where Sumatra is located). During which leg of the three-corner trade route did skippers pass these places?

   ❑ East Coast to Pacific Coast   ❑ Pacific Coast to China   ☑ China to East Coast

8. Matthew Perry opened trade with Japan in 1854. Which of these Asian countries is closer to America's Pacific Coast?

   ❑ China   ☑ Japan

Whaling

9. The Bering Sea is the narrow body of water between the Soviet Union and Alaska that connects the Arctic and Pacific Oceans. What geographic line cuts through this sea?

   ☑ Arctic Circle   ❑ Antarctic Circle   ❑ equator

American Republic

Word Search

Write the answer to each question in the blank and then circle the answer in the puzzle. Answers can be found in any direction, backwards or forwards.

1. What tool from Bible times did American farmers use to reap grain? ___sickle___ p. 270

2. What export became the key to the South's economy? ___cotton___ p. 272

3. Who "stole" Britain's factory system and brought it to America? ___Slater___ pp. 274-75

4. What was the first product produced with interchangeable parts? ___guns___ p. 276

5. What do we call the ability to make large quantities of a product? ___mass production___ p. 276

6. Who organized a mill town for girls in Massachusetts? ___Lowell___ p. 276

7. What workers' organizations fought problems in the factories? ___labor unions___ p. 277

8. What captain was the first American to circumnavigate the earth? ___Gray___ p. 278

9. Where did the Americans corner the pepper trade? ___Sumatra___ p. 279

10. What commodore secured a trade agreement with Japan in 1854? ___Perry___ p. 279

11. What favorite beverage did Americans find in Brazil? ___coffee___ p. 279

12. What animal did Americans use to make scrimshaw? ___whale___ p. 279

13. What Yale president supported the Second Great Awakening? ___Dwight___ p. 281

14. What was the most common form of frontier revivals? ___camp meetings___ p. 281

15. What false religion took over many churches in New England? ___Unitarianism___ p. 282

16. Who was probably the most famous Unitarian minister? ___Channing___ p. 282

A	Q	C	L	A	B	O	R	U	N	I	O	N	S	O
R	D	H	A	L	G	N	E	W	E	N	B	S	C	A
T	M	A	S	S	P	R	O	D	U	C	T	I	O	N
A	G	N	Y	G	U	L	L	E	W	O	L	C	F	O
M	U	N	Y	R	R	E	P	L	U	C	K	K	F	T
U	N	I	T	A	R	I	A	N	I	S	M	L	E	T
S	S	N	E	Y	U	C	K	W	H	A	L	E	E	O
A	S	G	N	I	T	E	E	M	P	M	A	C	K	C
B	U	S	L	A	T	E	R	T	H	G	I	W	D	K

American Republic

Map Study: Manifest Destiny

Refer to the maps in the textbook on pages 646-47, 287, 295, 298, and 300 to complete the map on the next page.

1. Label these rivers: Missouri, Platte, Snake, Columbia, Willamette, Sacramento, Arkansas, Rio Grande, Red, Nueces, Colorado.

2. Label these territories: Minnesota, Nebraska, Oregon, Utah, New Mexico, Kansas, Indian.

3. Label these states: Texas, California.

4. Label these cities with a dot: Independence, St. Joseph, Council Bluffs, Santa Fe, Salt Lake City, Astoria, Sacramento, San Francisco, San Diego, New Orleans.

5. Label these forts with a diamond: Ft. Leavenworth, Ft. Kearney, Ft. Hall, Bent's Fort.

6. Label these battle sites with a star: Alamo, San Jacinto, Palo Alto, Monterrey, Buena Vista, Veracruz, Mexico City.

7. Label these trails on the key: Oregon, Mormon, Santa Fe, California.

8. Using two colored pencils, draw a line for these military routes with an arrow at the end:

    • Zachary Taylor's advance from the mouth of the Nueces River to Buena Vista   *pp. 295-97*
    • Winfield Scott's advance from New Orleans to Mexico City   *p. 298*

9. Label these territory borders: 54°40', 49°, 42°.

Map Questions: Rivers and Forts

Answer these questions with the help of the textbook and the maps on pages 287 and 298.

1. What major rivers did the Oregon Trail follow? _*Platte, Snake, Columbia   p. 287*_

2. What river did the Mormon Trail share with the Oregon Trail? _*Platte   p. 287*_

3. What river did the California Trail follow? _*Humboldt   p. 287*_

4. What major river did the Santa Fe Trail follow? _*Arkansas   pp. 287, 298*_

5. Give two reasons the trails ran close to rivers. _*grass, water, clear landmarks   pp. 285-86*_

6. What fort was built at the base of the Santa Fe and Oregon trails? _*Ft. Leavenworth   p. 287*_

7. What fort was located at the major turn in the Santa Fe Trail? _*Bent's Fort   p. 287*_

8. What fort was located at the split of the Oregon and California trails? _*Ft. Hall   p. 287*_

9. What do you think was the main factor in placing forts? _*central location   pp. 285-90*_

10. What three rivers in Oregon aided its settlement? _*Snake, Columbia, Willamette   p. 287*_

11. What rivers were once a portion of Texas's boundary? _*Arkansas, Red, Nueces, Rio Grande   p. 298*_

12. Why do rivers make good boundaries? _*They are easy to mark.*_

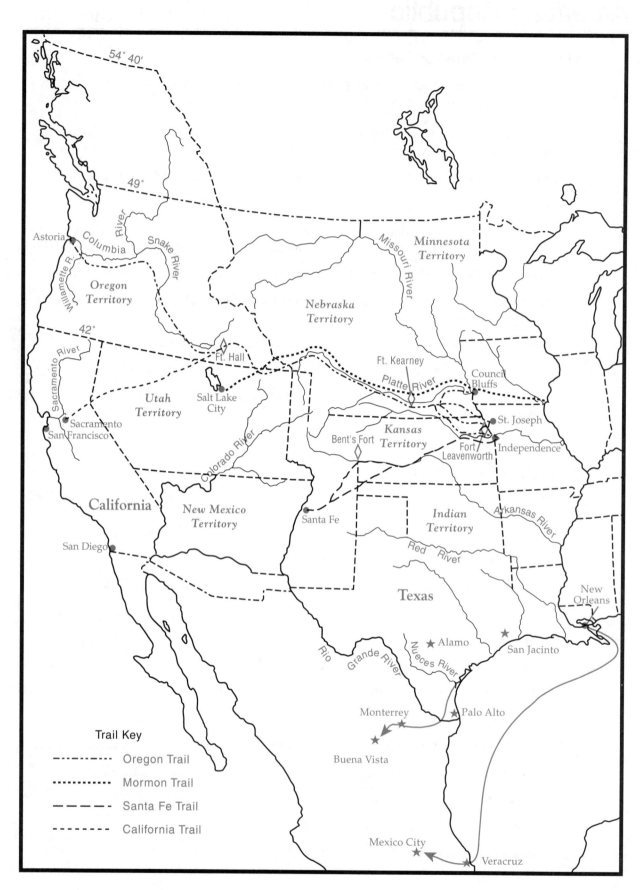

Trail Key

---·--- Oregon Trail

············ Mormon Trail

— — — Santa Fe Trail

-------- California Trail

American Republic

Trails to the West   ☆ *Classroom discussion*

For each trail, write the date given in the text for its first use, the town(s) at its start, the forts and landmarks on the trail, one town at its end, its original use or purpose, its main advantages, its main weaknesses, its significance in the settlement of the West, and its significance in the Mexican War.

	Santa Fe Trail pp. 286-88	Oregon Trail pp. 287-90	Mormon Trail pp. 285-87	California Trail p. 290
Date	1812	1812-1813 (1824)	1846-1847	1846
Town(s) at the Starting Point	Independence	Independence St. Joseph Council Bluffs	Nauvoo (Council Bluffs)	same as Oregon Trail
Forts and Landmarks on the Trail	Bent's Fort	Ft. Kearney & Ft. Hall Independence Rock South Pass	Ft. Kearney Independence Rock South Pass	same as Oregon Trail
Town at the Destination	Santa Fe	Astoria	Salt Lake City	Sacramento
Original Purpose	trade with Mexico	fur trapping	escape persecution	mountain men (trapping)
Main Advantages	first route to Mexico; one branch along rivers; patrols from Ft. Leavenworth	variety of starting points and destinations; numerous rivers	use of Oregon Trail; safe, isolated valley	major overland route to California
Main Weaknesses	poor relations with Mexico; Indian raids; unreliable water	long distance; cold weather; dry regions; high mountains	cold weather; dry regions	same as Oregon Trail; desert sand
Significance in Western Settlement		settlement of Oregon; missionary work in Oregon	Mormon settlement of Utah	movement of settlers and gold seekers to California
Significance in Mexican War	movement of troops and supplies to Mexico and California p. 297			

American Republic

Chapter 15   Activity C

The Consequences of War

The year 1846 was a pivotal year in American history. The Mexican War brought new opportunities and problems. Complete this essay about the war's causes and consequences.

By 1840 Americans believed they had a God-given (1) ___Manifest Destiny   p. 284___ to expand to the Pacific, including the Southwest. Led by (2) ___Stephen Austin   p. 291___, families began to settle in Texas because of cheap land, no taxes, and protection from (3) ___bills/debts   p. 291___ they owed in the States. As settlers poured in, Mexico's president, (4) ___Santa Anna   p. 291___, tried to regain control by force. The Texans declared independence and elected (5) ___Sam Houston   p. 294___ their new president. The provisional government, called the (6) ___Lone Star Republic   p. 294___, spent nine years seeking formal (7) ___annexation   p. 294___ as a new state in the Union. When Congress delayed because it feared war with (8) ___Mexico   p. 294___, the dark horse candidate (9) ___James Polk   p. 294___ ran for president on the popular pledge, "All of (10) ___Oregon   p. 294___, All of Texas." He appealed to both southerners and northerners who dreamed of western expansion.

The brief Mexican War, settled by the Treaty of (11) ___Guadalupe Hidalgo   p. 299___ in 1848, succeeded beyond America's wildest dreams. The settlement of Oregon's boundary at the (12) ___49th   p. 302___ parallel and the (13) ___Gadsden   p. 300___ Purchase in the Southwest completed America's acquisition of contiguous territory. The western trappers, known as the (14) ___mountain men   p. 301___, were overrun by settlers with "Oregon fever." The discovery of gold in 1848 by (15) ___James Marshall   p. 303___, who was preparing a sawmill for (16) ___John Sutter   p. 303___, started the famous (17) ___California   p. 304___ Gold Rush. In just over one year, the former Mexican territory had enough citizens to apply for statehood.

The request for statehood sparked a raging debate in Congress. Many northerners had opposed the Mexican War because they did not want the South to extend (18) ___slavery   p. 305___ to the territories. Congressman (19) ___Stephen Douglas   p. 306___ pushed through five separate bills to settle the debate. The bills, known as the (20) ___Compromise of 1850   p. 305___, were signed by the Whig president (21) ___Millard Fillmore   p. 306___. California was admitted as a free state, while the territories of New Mexico and (22) ___Utah   p. 306___ were allowed to decide whether they wanted slavery, according to a principle known as (23) ___popular sovereignty   p. 306___. America entered the 1850s as a sharply divided nation, held together by the moderate Northern Democrats, called (24) ___Doughfaces   p. 306___, and their president, (25) ___Franklin Pierce   p. 306___.

American Republic

War Memos

Pretend you are the American commander in each of these battles or campaigns. Give your name and a brief summary of the battle or campaign. (In the case of Jim Bowie, write his last account before he died.) Then pretend you are a modern historian in the war department in Washington, D.C., who must tell the significance of the battle.

MEMO   United States War Department
Washington, D.C.

Commanding Officer: _*Jim Bowie (William Travis)*_   Date: _*February 1836*_

Location: _*the Alamo, San Antonio   pp. 291-93*_

Summary: _*Only 183 men defended the mission thirteen days against more than four thousand Mexican troops. Every man vowed to fight valiantly to the last.*_

Significance: _*The massacre inspired the Texans to declare independence and to seek revenge.*_

MEMO   United States War Department
Washington, D.C.

Commanding Officer: _*Sam Houston*_   Date: _*21 April 1836*_

Location: _*San Jacinto   pp. 293-94*_

Summary: _*I carefully planned a battle on the plain with my eight-hundred-man army. The attack took Santa Anna completely by surprise. In twenty minutes almost the entire Mexican army of fourteen hundred was captured or killed, and Santa Anna became a hostage.*_

Significance: _*Texas used the hostage Santa Anna to prevent further attacks, and the "Lone Star Republic" became a reality.*_

MEMO United States War Department
Washington, D.C.

Commanding Officer: _John Charles Frémont_   Date: _Summer 1846_

Location: _California Campaign   p. 297_

Summary: _With the help of some settlers and the Pacific Squadron, a "Bear Flag Revolution" occurred. We easily captured the entire region._

Significance: _The United States was able to claim and settle California after the war. The new territory increased North-South tension over slavery.   p. 299_

MEMO United States War Department
Washington, D.C.

Commanding Officer: _Zachary Taylor_   Date: _22-23 February 1847_

Location: _Buena Vista, Mexico   p. 297_

Summary: _After my successful capture of Monterrey, Santa Anna surprised my army. We were forced to burn our supplies and retreat to a sheep ranch. There a thunderstorm and a brisk counterattack saved us despite three-to-one odds._

Significance: _"Old Rough and Ready" became a hero, and the people elected him president of the U.S.   p. 305_

MEMO United States War Department
Washington, D.C.

Commanding Officer: _Winfield Scott_   Date: _September 1847_

Location: _Mexico City Campaign   pp. 298-99_

Summary: _After taking Veracruz, our way to Mexico City was blocked by Santa Anna's reorganized army. We found a route around the mountains and attacked him from the side. After four minor battles, his panicked army surrendered._

Significance: _This victory forced Mexico to sign the Treaty of Guadalupe Hidalgo._

American Republic
Chapter 16   Activity A

Differences Between the North and the South ☆ *Classroom discussion*

Complete the chart. Write a key word or phrase that shows the major differences between the North and the South.   *pp. 312-13*

		North	South
Economic Differences	**Agriculture**	small farms	cotton plantations
	Industry	most of the nation's factories	few factories
	Source of Labor	immigrant	slaves
Social Differences	**Main Occupations**	merchants, factory workers, small farmers	farmers, traders of agricultural products
	Population Centers	many large, growing cities	few villages, towns, or cities
	Ruling Class	owners of factories and other businesses	plantation owners
	Education	public education	private education
Political Differences	**Role of Government**	support of strong central government; many government services	fear of strong central government; emphasis on local and state government; few local services
	Collection of Taxes	willingness to pay taxes for services	no need or ability to pay taxes for services
	Rights of States	federal supremacy	states' rights of nullification
	Role of Tariffs	high tariff to protect industry	low tariff and cheap foreign goods

American Republic

Chapter 16   Activity B

Slavery: America's Great Debate

In two or three sentences summarize each characteristic of American slavery discussed in your text, pages 314-18. Your summary should include the terms listed with each topic.

1. How were slaves acquired? Why did emancipation fail? (Terms: "middle passage," emancipation)

   The first slaves were captured on Africa's western coast and shipped across the Atlantic

   on the inhumane "middle passage." Although the slave trade was banned in 1808, the

   South's slave population kept increasing due to the growth of families. The idea of the

   emancipation of slaves became unpopular in the South after the invention of the cotton gin.   pp. 314-

2. How were slaves treated? (Terms: house slaves, field slaves, "sold down river")

   The treatment of slaves depended on the plantation. Most house slaves were treated

   better than field slaves. The slaves had few luxuries, and their greatest fear was being

   "sold down river" to the deadly sugar cane plantations.   p. 317

3. What were the northern views of slavery? (Terms: abolitionism, compensated emancipation, William Lloyd Garrison)

   Supporters of abolitionism, such as the editor William Lloyd Garrison, wanted to do away

   with slavery completely. Others favored compensated emancipation, whereby the slave

   owner would be paid for the loss of his property. Although they were against slavery,

   most northerners were still prejudiced.   p. 316

4. What were the southern views of slavery? (Terms: necessary evil, highland)

   Most southerners defended slavery as a necessary evil in a cotton-producing culture.

   Some highland farmers in the Appalachians, Kentucky, and Tennessee opposed slavery.

   pp. 316-17

5. What were the black responses to slavery? (Terms: Underground Railroad, slave rebellions, Frederick Douglass, Harriet Tubman)

   Some slaves tried to run away to freedom in Canada through the illegal Underground

   Railroad. Others attempted slave rebellions but failed. Some black leaders in the North,

   such as Frederick Douglass, lectured in support of abolitionism; and other leaders, such

   as Harriet Tubman, supported the Underground Railroad.   pp. 317-18

American Republic

Steps to War

In Chapter 12 you studied the northern actions and southern reactions during the nullification crisis of 1828. That crisis was solved peacefully, but a new crisis during the 1850s led to war. Complete the chart with the answers listed on the back.

Cause	Event	Southern Reaction
Processing cotton with slaves is unprofitable. p. 315	invention of cotton gin (1793)	*Slavery becomes profitable and widespread.*
The North wants a balance of slave states and free states.	Compromise of 1820	The South expects all new lands below 36° 30' to become slave states.
The abolitionist movement begins. p. 316	founding of *The Liberator* (1831)	*Southerners begin to defend slavery as a necessary evil.*
Slaves support revolt. p. 317	Nat Turner's rebellion (1831)	*Southerners become stricter with blacks.*
S.C. nullifies Tariff of Abominations and Jackson's Force Bill.	Compromise of 1833	The question of states' rights remains unsettled.
Americans fight the Mexican War to achieve Manifest Destiny.	Mexican Cession (1848)	The South desires an equal share of the new territories.
The North wants the Mexican Cession to become free states.	Compromise of 1850	The South demands enforcement of the strict Fugitive Slave Law.
Writers describe the plight of fugitive slaves. p. 319	*Uncle Tom's Cabin* (1851)	*Southerners resent the implication that their society is evil.*
Early pro-Union leaders die. p. 321	loss of compromisers (1852)	*Weak new leaders fail to provide solutions.*
Popular sovereignty applies to territories north of 36° 30'. p. 319	Kansas-Nebraska Act (1854)	*Proslavery groups fight in Bleeding Kansas.*
The Whig Party splits over slavery in Kansas. pp. 319-20	new Republican party (1854)	*Southerners support a moderate Democrat in the 1856 election.*
Lawyers question the rights of slaves in the territories. pp. 320-21	Dred Scott decision (1857)	*The courts rule that territories cannot ban slavery.*
Northern fanatics try to stop slavery by force. pp. 321-22	John Brown's raid (1859)	*Southerners hang a northern abolitionist.*
Fire-eaters divide the Democratic Party. p. 322	Lincoln's election (1860)	*Fire-eaters form the Confederate States of America.*
The president says all forts are federal property. p. 325	resupply of Ft. Sumter (1861)	*The Confederates shell a federal fort.*

Causes

The Whig Party splits over slavery in Kansas.
The abolitionist movement begins.
Fire-eaters divide the Democratic Party.
Slaves support revolt.
Northern fanatics try to stop slavery by force.
Lawyers question the rights of slaves in the territories.
The president says all forts are federal property.
Popular sovereignty applies to territories north of 36° 30'.
Processing cotton with slaves is unprofitable.
Early pro-Union leaders die.
Writers describe the plight of fugitive slaves.

Southern Reactions

The courts rule that territories cannot ban slavery.
Southerners resent the implication that their society is evil.
Fire-eaters form the Confederate States of America.
Southerners become stricter with blacks.
Southerners support a moderate Democrat in the 1856 election.
Slavery becomes profitable and widespread.
The Confederates shell a federal fort.
Weak new leaders fail to provide solutions.
Southerners begin to defend slavery as a necessary evil.
Proslavery groups fight in Bleeding Kansas.
Southerners hang a northern abolitionist.

Review Questions

Answer these questions based on the textbook and the chart on the previous page.

1. During what three years did the South accept major compromises? ___1820, 1833, 1850___

2. No longer willing to compromise, what three parties from the North joined the antislavery Republican Party? _Conscience Whigs, Free Soilers, northern Democrats___ p. 319

3. What compromise did a Southern chief justice invalidate in 1857? _Missouri Compromise___ p. 320

4. Why do you think the South was more upset by John Brown's revolt than Nat Turner's? ___The North treated Brown as a martyr.___ p. 322

5. What was the first state to secede after Lincoln's election? ___South Carolina___ p. 323

6. Why did Lincoln want the South to fire the first shot? _Lincoln did not want the border states to consider him an invader.___ pp. 325-26

7. What forced Virginia, Arkansas, and Tennessee to choose sides? ___Lincoln's call for troops___ p. 326

8. What Southern state split into two opposing states during the Civil War? _Virginia___ p. 326

9. What four border states eventually joined the Union? _Delaware, Maryland, Kentucky, Missouri___ p. 326

American Republic

Case #3: The Search for King Cotton

Mastermind Sarah Bellum is on the loose in the southern United States. Known to the world and the GIA as Auntie Bellum, the criminal has plans to unleash her new mutant pet—King Cotton. King Cotton is a mix between a thirty-foot gorilla and a giant cotton ball. If released, Cotton could bring new meaning to the word *reconstruction* in the South. Auntie Bellum is well aware that Sir Vey is trying to catch her. She's been taunting him by sending clues to her location. The first clue reveals the location of the next, and so on, until the final one reveals where Bellum and Cotton are hiding out. Sir Vey must figure out the clues and get to Bellum before it's too late for the South. Use the maps and text from Chapters 11 through 16 and the map of the South on page 333 to help Sir Vey capture Auntie Bellum.

Clue #1: We're in the state capital closest to where the Battle of Horseshoe Bend was fought in 1814. _____Montgomery____pp. 220-21_____

Clue #2: We've moved to the capital of the state in the South considered a border state in the Civil War. _____Frankfort____pp. 326, 333_____

Clue #3: Missed us! Now we're in the city that was close to where the Cane Ridge camp meeting took place in 1801. _____Lexington____p. 281_____

Clue #4: We've gone to the city in Georgia where the Great Wagon Road ended.
_____Augusta____p. 256_____

Clue #5: You're slow. We're headed for the city linked to western Virginia by the James River and Kanawha canal. _____Richmond____p. 261_____

Clue #6: We like the coast better. We're sunning in the coastal city in the southern state that applied for statehood in 1817. __Biloxi   p. 220__

Clue #7: Sorry we missed you. Our new hotel is in the state capital on the Arkansas River.
__Little Rock   p. 333__

Clue #8: After visiting the Alamo, we're in the city closest to where the battles of Palo Alto and Resaca de la Palma were fought. __Brownsville   pp. 298, 333__

Clue #9: If you want to stay on our trail, try meeting us in the city where the Civil War started on April 12, 1861. __Charleston, South Carolina   p. 326__

Clue #10: That was close! But I doubt you'll catch us in the city farthest south in the southern states. __Key West   p. 333__

Clue #11: You think you're clever, Sir Vey, but you won't find the southern city that prior to the Civil War had a population of approximately 150,000. __New Orleans   p. 312__

Clue #12: Clever, yes, but not quick enough. We're visiting the city south of Charleston, South Carolina, that was a major railroad center in 1860. __Savannah   p. 264__

Clue #13: Remember the Alamo? But I don't think you'll catch us in the city where it's located.
__San Antonio   p. 292__

Clue #14: You'll have to be quick. Try going to the city in Texas located between the Canadian and Red Rivers. __Amarillo   p. 333__

Clue #15: So long, Sir Vey. Now we've gone to the capital of the state where James Polk was born. __Raleigh   pp. 295, 333__

Clue #16: You're getting close, Sir Vey, but not close enough. Try to catch us in the capital of the southern state that was a territory at the time of the Civil War. __Oklahoma City   p. 327__

Clue #17: We're long gone on our way to the city that was once the western end of the Wilderness Road. __Louisville   p. 255__

Clue #18: If you've gotten this far, you're smarter than I thought, Sir Vey. Look for the next clue in the capital of the state where Zachary Taylor was born. __Richmond   pp. 303, 333__

Clue #19: Now head to the state capital that is approximately 150 miles from Huntsville, Alabama. __Atlanta   p. 333__

Clue #20: I doubt you've figured out all those clues, Sir Vey. So King Cotton and I will launch our attack from the city named after the first president of the Lone Star Republic.
__Houston   p. 294__

American Republic

Map Study: Civil War

Refer to the maps in the textbook on pages 646-47, 327, 339, 344, 346, 351, and 353 to complete the map on the next page.

1. Label these rivers: Mississippi, Ohio, Cumberland, Tennessee, James, Potomac.

2. With a blue pencil, label these Union states with their abbreviations: Pennsylvania (PA), West Virginia (WV), Ohio (OH), Indiana (IN), Illinois (IL).

3. With a red pencil, label these border states with their abbreviations: Maryland (MD), Kentucky (KY), Missouri (MO).

4. With a black pencil, label these Confederate states with their abbreviations: Virginia (VA), North Carolina (NC), South Carolina (SC), Georgia (GA), Florida (FL), Alabama (AL), Tennessee (TN), Mississippi (MS), Arkansas (AR), Louisiana (LA), Texas (TX).

5. Label these capitals with a star: Washington, D.C.; Richmond.

6. Label these cities with a black dot: New York (N.Y.), Frankfort (Ky.), Cairo (Ill.), Savannah (Ga.), Columbia (S.C.), Durham (N.C.), Appomattox Courthouse (Va.).

7. Label these battle sites with a red dot: Fort Henry, Shiloh, New Orleans, Vicksburg, Petersburg, Manassas, Antietam, Chancellorsville, Gettysburg, Chattanooga, Atlanta.

8. The Union had two main armies operating in the West and one main army in the East. Small cavalry and naval forces performed many other tasks. With a blue pencil, draw a line for these military campaigns with an arrow at the end:

   • Army of the Cumberland: from Cairo through Fort Henry, Shiloh, Chattanooga, and Savannah to Durham

   • Army of the Mississippi: from Cairo to Vicksburg

   • Army of the Potomac in 1862 (McClellan's Peninsular Campaign): from Washington, D.C., to Richmond

   • Army of the Potomac in 1864-65 (Grant's War of Attrition): from Virginia's Wilderness through Petersburg to Appomattox

   • Farragut's Western Gulf Squadron in 1862-63: from New Orleans to Vicksburg

   • Sheridan's Cavalry Corps in 1864-65: Shenandoah Valley

9. The Confederates had two main armies in the West and one in the East. Usually these armies were on the defensive. On three occasions, however, an army tried to move north. With a black pencil, draw a line with an arrow at the end for these military campaigns:

   • Bragg's Army of the Tennessee in 1862: from Shiloh to Frankfort

   • Lee's Army of Northern Virginia in 1862: from Manassas to Antietam

   • Lee's Army of Northern Virginia in 1863: from Chancellorsville to Gettysburg

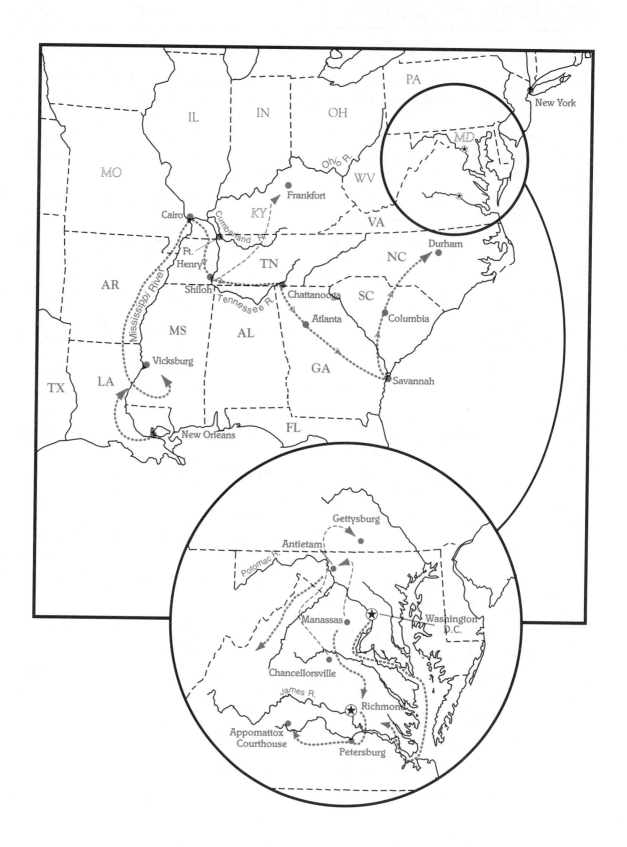

American Republic

Major Battles

Complete the chart. For each battle, include the commander of each side, if he is mentioned in the text. Also place an asterisk (*) beside each battle that the Union clearly won.

	Battle	Year	Leaders	Significance
Early Campaigns	First Battle of Bull Run p. 340	1861	Irvin McDowell Joseph E. Johnston	Lincoln asked McClellan to forge a strong army; the South became overconfident; Jackson won fame as "Stonewall."
	Monitor vs. *Merrimac* p. 338	1862		Ironclad ships proved their superiority in warfare to wooden ships.
	Second Battle of Bull Run pp. 341-42	1862	John Pope Robert E. Lee	The North restored McClellan as commander; the South reached its high tide.
Western Campaigns	*Fort Henry & Fort Donelson p. 343	1862	Ulysses S. Grant	The North gained control of the Tennessee and Cumberland rivers (upper Mississippi region).
	*New Orleans p. 344	1862	David Glasgow Farragut (Benjamin Butler)	The North gained control of the lower Mississippi.
	*Vicksburg p. 344	1863	Ulysses S. Grant Joseph Pemberton	The North gained complete control of the Mississippi.
Eastern Campaigns	Antietam p. 345	1862	George B. McClellan Robert E. Lee	The North stopped Lee's first offensive; Lincoln issued the Emancipation Proclamation; Britain stayed out of the war.
	Chancellorsville pp. 345-47	1863	"Fighting Joe" Hooker Robert E. Lee	The South won its finest victory of the war; Jackson died; Lee planned a second invasion north.
	*Gettysburg p. 347	1863	George Gordon Meade Robert E. Lee	The North stopped Lee's offensive; Pickett's charge was a failure; Grant became supreme commander.
Final Campaigns	Shenandoah Valley raid p. 349	1864-65	Philip Sheridan Jubal Early	The North stopped Early's raids; Sheridan destroyed the source of food for Lee's starving army.
	*March to the Sea pp. 350-51	1864	William T. Sherman	The North destroyed Georgia's spirit and resources; pillaging by bummers caused great bitterness.
	*Appomattox Courthouse p. 354	1865	Ulysses S. Grant Robert E. Lee	After losing the battle for Petersburg, Lee's army was outnumbered and trapped. Lee's army surrendered.

Answer these questions based on the chart.

1. Which commander fought the most battles? __Robert E. Lee__

2. In which region did the Union win every major battle? __the West__

3. What Confederate victory came before Antietam? __Second Battle of Bull Run__

4. What battle was the most significant turning point in the war? __Answers will vary.__

5. What was the last major Confederate victory in the war? __Chancellorsville__

American Republic

Chapter 17   Activity C

Pie Graphs: Northern Advantages During the Civil War

Below is a chart showing the relative differences between the North and the South at the outset of the Civil War. Based on the chart, calculate the South's piece of each "pie." Draw the line at the right place and shade the South's piece. The first one is done for you.

	Railroads	Factories	Population	Farmland	Iron	Currency
North	72%	85%	71%	65%	96%	81%
South	28%	15%	29%	35%	4%	19%

Railroads

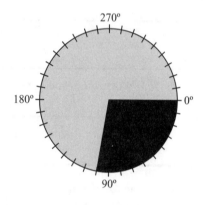

360° x .28 = 100°

Factories

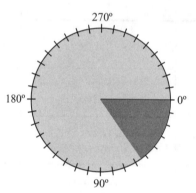

360° x .15 = 54 °

Population

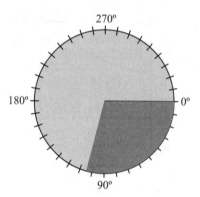

360° x .29 = 104 °

Farmland

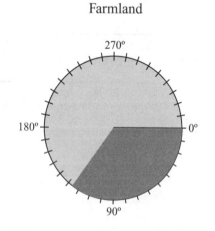

360° x .35 = 126 °

Iron

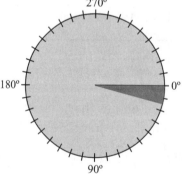

360° x .04 = 14 °

Currency

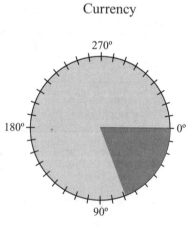

360° x .19 = 68 °

American Republic

Chapter 17   Activity D

Trivia Game: Abraham Lincoln

Except for the bonus questions, you can find the answers to these trivia questions in the text. Some are harder than others. Use the index starting on page 650 of the text to help you since several answers are not in Chapter 17.

Five Points

1. Where was Lincoln born? _Hodgenville, Kentucky   p. 324_

2. On what date was Lincoln born? _February 12, 1809   p. 324_

3. What was the name of Lincoln's wife? _Mary Todd   p. 324_

4. How many children did Lincoln have? _4   p. 324_

5. What was Lincoln's occupation before he became president? _lawyer   p. 324_

6. To what political party did President Lincoln belong? _Republican   p. 324_

7. At what ceremony did Lincoln give the Gettysburg Address? _cemetery dedication   p. 348_

8. After what victory did Lincoln issue the Emancipation Proclamation? _Battle of Antietam   p. 345_

9. How many Confederate states quit fighting because of the Emancipation Proclamation? _0   p. 348_

10. Who was Lincoln's vice president during his second term? _Andrew Johnson   p. 352_

11. Who assassinated Lincoln? _John Wilkes Booth   p. 356_

12. What was the name of the theater where Lincoln was assassinated? _Ford's Theater   pp. 355-56_

Ten Points

13. How many debates did Lincoln have with Senator Stephen Douglas in 1858? _7   p. 323_

14. How many southern states did Lincoln win during the election of 1860? _0   p. 323_

15. What fort did Lincoln try to resupply in 1861, sparking the Civil War? _Ft. Sumter   pp. 325-26_

16. Whom did Lincoln ask to command the Union army after the First Battle of Bull Run?
    George McClellan   p. 340

17. What did Lincoln read from the War Department before bed each night? _war dispatches from the front lines   p. 338_

18. During what speech did Lincoln use the phrase "government of the people, by the people, for the people"? _Gettysburg Address   p. 348_

19. What "present" did Sherman give Lincoln after his March to the Sea? _Savannah   pp. 351-52_

20. Who ran against Lincoln on a peace ticket in the election of 1864? _George McClellan   p. 352_

21. About whom did Lincoln say, "I cannot spare this man. He wins"? _Grant   p. 354_

22. During what siege did Lincoln tell Grant, "Hold on with a bulldog grip and chew and choke as much as possible"? _Petersburg   p. 354_

Fifteen Points

23. For what invention did Lincoln receive a patent? ___*hydraulic lift*   *p. 324*___

24. Lincoln received the first telegraph message across the continent. What did it tell him?
    ___*California would stay in the Union.*   *p. 266*___ .

25. How many commanders in the East did Lincoln go through before he settled on Grant?___*7*___ *p. 329*

26. Who was Lincoln's powerful secretary of state? ___*William Seward*   *p. 371*___

27. What plan did Lincoln announce in December 1863 to restore the South to the Union?
    ___*Ten Percent Plan*   *p. 362*___

28. What famous railroad system did Congress charter in 1864 during Lincoln's administration?
    ___*first transcontinental railroad*   *p. 393*___

29. During what speech did Lincoln say, "With malice toward none; with charity for all"?
    ___*Second Inaugural Address*   *p. 360*___

Bonus Questions (Twenty Points)

30. How tall was Lincoln?___*6' 4"*___

31. What was Lincoln's average weight? ___*180 pounds*___

32. What was the name of Lincoln's mother, who died of "milk sickness"? ___*Nancy Hanks*___

33. Lincoln apparently said of his stepmother, "God bless my mother; all that I am or ever
    hope to be I owe to her." What was her name?___*Sarah Bush Johnston*___

34. What eleven-year-old girl suggested that Lincoln grow a beard? ___*Grace Bedell*___

35. Which of Lincoln's sons died while Lincoln was president? ___*William "Willie" Wallace*___

36. What Scripture verse was Lincoln alluding to when he said, "A house divided against
    itself cannot stand"? ___*Mark 3:25 (Matthew 12:25)*___

37. What constitutional amendment passed during Lincoln's administration? ___*Thirteenth*___

38. What play was Lincoln watching at his assassination? ___*Our American Cousin*___

39. What cabinet member was stabbed (but survived) the night of Lincoln's assassination?
    ___*Seward*___

40. What two speeches are carved into the side chambers at the Lincoln Memorial?
    ___*Gettysburg Address; Second Inaugural Address*___

41. What American poet wrote a six-volume biography of Lincoln? ___*Carl Sandburg*___

42. What holiday do we celebrate to honor Lincoln? ___*President's Day*___

American Republic

Types of History

"War makes good history," said novelist Thomas Hardy. Below are some events that influenced the Civil War. Match each event with the type of history it is.

A. Military history: armies, navies, commanders, soldiers, battles, campaigns
B. Political history: government relations, unfair laws, riots, elections, foreign affairs
C. Economic history: trade, industry, workers, farming, new technology
D. Social history: family life, personal hardships, race relations, immigrants, photography

__D__ 1. The Civil War split families throughout the United States, including the family of Senator John Crittenden.

__A__ 2. Soldiers spent sixty percent of their time in camp, five percent fighting.

__D__ 3. Northerners often hired immigrants to serve as substitutes for them in the draft.

__B__ 4. Northerners were angry at the government's unfair draft laws, and a four-day riot occurred in New York.

__B__ 5. The Confederate "Twenty-Negro Law" exempted rich slave owners from the draft.

__D__ 6. Northern white people did not treat black people fairly. They kept them out of the army until 1863, and even then they gave black soldiers the worst tasks.

__C__ 7. Northern businesses relied on women and a large pool of immigrants to work in their factories.

__C__ 8. Farm production increased during the war because farmers began purchasing new machinery.

__C__ 9. The Union blockade cut off most of the South's trade. As a result, the South could not get money for its cotton, and basic items became very expensive.

__D__ 10. Daily life in the South became increasingly difficult as the war progressed, and the people had to live without many basic foods.

__D__ 11. Southerners had to make unusual substitutes for food they could not buy. For instance, peanuts and sweet potatoes were used to make coffee.

__B__ 12. The Confederate government became so desperate towards the end of the war that it used taxes in kind. Tax collectors demanded corn and hogs, not dollars and cents.

__A/C__ 13. For the first time in history, modern industry and technology became a critical factor in war. Both sides used telegraphs, trains, mines, rifled guns, and ironclad ships.

__D__ 14. Mathew Brady, the most famous photographer of the Civil War, captured images from the war for people back home.

__A__ 15. General Winfield Scott created the "Anaconda Plan," the Union's basic strategy of strangling the South with a naval blockade and the capture of the Mississippi River.

__C__ 16. The Civil War greatly benefited the ship-building industry in the Northeast. The United States emerged from the conflict with one of the strongest fleets in the world.

__C__ 17. Southern businessmen relied on blockade runners to carry goods in and out of Confederate ports. These daring ships made huge profits, but they could not meet all of the South's needs.

__A__ 18. Sailors in the Union blockade received little glory for their work, but they were a great help to the war effort.

__A__ 19. The Union army in the East had five different commanders in 1863.

__A__ 20. Pickett's charge during the Battle of Gettysburg shows the courage of Lee's army against hopeless odds.

__B__ 21. One purpose of Lincoln's Gettysburg Address was to explain the reason that so many Americans had died for their government.

__B/D__ 22. For over a hundred years schoolchildren have read and even memorized Lincoln's Gettysburg Address. It states the basic principles of freedom and democracy for which our forefathers have sacrificed their lives.

__B__ 23. One reason for Lincoln's Emancipation Proclamation was a diplomatic effort to keep Great Britain from joining the South.

__D__ 24. Even though the Emancipation Proclamation limited its freedoms to the Confederate-controlled territories, it became an important document in the public acceptance of racial equality everywhere.

__D__ 25. Americans wrote some memorable music during this time, such as Julia Ward Howe's "Battle Hymn of the Republic."

__D__ 26. The destructiveness of Union deserters and bummers during the March to the Sea created bitterness in the South and hurt relations between both regions for generations to come.

__B__ 27. The presidential election of 1864 was perhaps the greatest opportunity that the South had to win the war. More important than Southern victories on the battlefield were the Northern civilians who could choose a new president with a "peace ticket."

__B__ 28. One evidence of Lincoln's political skill was his selection of Andrew Johnson, a Southerner, as his vice president in 1864.

__A-D__ 29. Grant's generous terms of surrender at Appomattox helped to reunite the people into one nation again. Grant gave the Confederate soldiers supplies and let them keep their horses for farm work.

__D__ 30. Practically every family in America attended a funeral for one relative or close friend during the war. The hardships of the war left deep scars on everyone involved.

__B/D__ 31. Even though he was president, Lincoln took the time to send personal notes to some of the families whose sons had died during the war. One of the most moving examples is his letter to Mrs. Bixby of Massachusetts.

__C/D__ 32. Southern farms, businesses, and railroads were destroyed by the Civil War. It took almost a century for the southern economy to recover completely.

__B/D__ 33. The greatest personal tragedy of the Civil War was probably Lincoln's assassination by John Wilkes Booth. Everyone in the North and the South suffered either directly or indirectly from his untimely death.

American Republic

Chapter 18   Activity A

Time Line of Reconstruction

Your book covers the three phases of Reconstruction in sections 2, 3, and 4. Place each event in the correct section and year. Then give the event's significance in Reconstruction.

Civil Rights Act (first)	Ten Percent Plan	Tenure of Office Act
Thirteenth Amendment	Johnson's Plan	General Amnesty Act
Fourteenth Amendment	Freedmen's Bureau	Wade-Davis Bill
Fifteenth Amendment	Disputed Election	Troops Withdrawn from S.C.
Reconstruction Act		

	Year	Event	Significance
President (2)	1863	Ten Percent Plan p. 362	Congress rejected Lincoln's plan to admit states if ten percent of the voters swore allegiance.
	1864	Wade-Davis Bill p. 363	Lincoln vetoed Congress's plan to admit states if fifty percent of the voters swore allegiance.
	1865	Johnson's Plan pp. 364, 368	Congress rejected Johnson's fifty percent plan because it was too lenient.
	1865	Thirteenth Amendment p. 364	Slavery was abolished.
	1865	Freedmen's Bureau p. 366	A federal relief agency helped refugees and started schools and hospitals for blacks.
Radical Republicans (3)	1866	Civil Rights Act p. 366	Congress gave blacks citizenship despite Johnson's veto.
	1866	Fourteenth Amendment pp. 366-67	People of all races became citizens; Congress assumed the right to pardon rebels. Johnson's stubborn opposition put the Radicals in power.
	1867	Reconstruction Act p. 368	Congress established military rule and a harsh plan to readmit states to the Union.
	1867	Tenure of Office Act pp. 369-70	Congress kept the president from removing officials. When Johnson resisted, the House impeached him.
	1870	Fifteenth Amendment p. 371	People of all races received full voting rights.
Redeemers (4)	1872	General Amnesty Act p. 373	Liberal Republicans persuaded Congress to pardon all but a few former Confederate leaders.
	1876	Disputed Election pp. 374, 376	To ensure his election, the Republican candidate promised to end Radical Reconstruction.
	1877	Troops Withdrawn from S.C. p. 376	Democrats took control of all southern state governments and of future Reconstruction.

American Republic

Chapter 18   Activity B

Problems in the Presidency

Match the presidents with the problems that are associated with them.

A. Abraham Lincoln   C. Ulysses S. Grant
B. Andrew Johnson   D. Rutherford B. Hayes

__D__ 1. To ensure his election, he bargained away most of his presidential power. *p. 376*

__B__ 2. He became president after the elected president was assassinated. *p. 363*

__A__ 3. Congress refused to accept his Ten Percent Plan. *pp. 362-63*

__A__ 4. He vetoed the Wade-Davis Bill. *p. 363*

__C__ 5. His two terms were marred by political corruption. *p. 372*

__B__ 6. He was the first president ever to be impeached. *p. 370*

__D__ 7. He became president even though his opponent won the popular vote. *p. 374*

__C__ 8. He did not prosecute the many corrupt politicians in government. *p. 372*

__A__ 9. An assassin killed the president soon after the president called for "charity for all." *p. 360*

__D__ 10. He was elected by eight Republicans in a special electoral commission. *p. 374*

__B__ 11. The Republican Party never accepted him because he was a pro-Democrat southerner. *pp. 363, 365*

__B__ 12. He was ridiculed for spending $7 million to purchase "Seward's Folly." *p. 371*

__C__ 13. He is rated as one of the worst presidents in American history. *p. 372*

__A__ 14. Congress accused him of exceeding his presidential powers during the war. *p. 363*

__B__ 15. His stubbornness drove moderate Republicans into the Radical camp. *p. 365*

__C__ 16. He was a heavy drinker. *p. 372*

__B__ 17. The Radicals gained control of Congress and Reconstruction during his term. *p. 366*

__B__ 18. He instituted his plan for Reconstruction while Congress was out of session. *p. 363*

__B__ 19. Congress passed the Reconstruction Act in spite of his veto. *p. 368*

__C__ 20. During his elections, the Radicals stirred up war hatred by "waving the bloody shirt." *p. 377*

Plans for Reconstruction

Complete the chart.

	Ten Percent Plan *p. 362*	Johnson's Plan *p. 364*	Wade-Davis Bill *p. 363*	Reconstruction Act *p. 368*
Percent of Voters Swearing Oath	*10%*	*50%*	*50%*	
Conditions for Pardons	*oath to support the Constitution and Union*	*oath to support the Union*	*oath that they never supported the Confederacy voluntarily*	*no voting rights to Confederate leaders (except by vote of Congress)*
Extra Conditions New States Must Accept	*none*	*repudiation of debts; ratification of Thirteenth Amendment*	*abolition of slavery; repudiation of debts and secession*	*open conventions with black delegates; ratification of Fourteenth Amendment*

Skills: Recognition/Charts

American Republic

Chapter 19   Activity A

Topic Sentences for "Materials and People"

The first sentence in each paragraph, called the *topic sentence,* tells you the main subject of the paragraph. Topic sentences give you a good summary of the paragraphs in each section. Write the topic sentences from the paragraphs at the beginning of Chapter 19 and under "Materials and People." (The first one has been done for you.)

Introduction to Chapter 19 and "Materials and People" (three topic sentences)

When the United States entered the nineteenth century, it was a quiet land with family farms,

small villages, and a few small cities on the Atlantic coastline. The late nineteenth century

was a time of growth for the nation, especially for its industries. The United States was

able to undergo such rapid changes for a variety of reasons.

_____

"Natural Resources" (four topic sentences)

One key to American industrial growth was its abundant natural resources. Great lodes of gold,

silver, and copper were found in the Rocky Mountains, the Far West, and Alaska. The rich iron

ore deposits of northern Minnesota, the Mesabi and Cayuna ranges, provided raw materials for

the growing iron and steel industries. Another important American resource was timber.

_____

_____

_____

_____

"Immigration Provides Labor" and "Immigrants Come to America" (five topic sentences)

Developing industries need workers. Before 1880 most of the immigrants came from

northwestern European countries like Britain, Ireland, Germany, or the Scandinavian countries,

and they were largely Protestant. Most Europeans crossed the Atlantic by the shortest and

cheapest routes. Some immigrants had been recruited in their homelands by agents of various

American companies in need of laborers. Employers eagerly hired immigrants.

_____

_____

_____

_____

_____

"Ellis Island and Ports of Entry" (three topic sentences)

The largest number of European immigrants came to America by way of New York harbor.

Some immigrants landed in Montreal; others, especially the Irish, came to Boston. Immigrants

often settled in neighborhoods of cities where others of their nationality lived.

"Immigrants Work to Build America" (eight topic sentences)

While immigrants came from many lands, Ireland provided a large number of them in the 1800s.

The Irish played important roles in the construction of America's canal and railroad systems.

Some Irishmen sought altogether different work. China also provided many immigrants

for America. Chinese immigrants continued to come, and as long as jobs were available,

Americans did not object too much to their arrival. Northern Europe also sent many of its

people to America. Scandinavians—Norwegians, Swedes, and Finns—also came to America.

The people of these and other ethnic groups contributed greatly to the American way of life.

American Republic

Chapter 19   Activity B

Map Study: Railroads, Resources, and Immigrants

Refer to the maps in the textbook on pages 264 and 395 to complete the map below.

1. Using a blue pencil, label these territories with their abbreviations: Dakota (DAK), Wyoming (WY), Montana (MT), Idaho (ID), Washington (WA), Utah (UT), Indian (IND), New Mexico (NM), Arizona (AZ).

2. Label these towns and cities: Boston, New York, Albany, Buffalo, Chicago, New Orleans, St. Joseph, Omaha, Duluth, Los Angeles, San Francisco, Tacoma.

3. Using a red pencil, draw these train routes:

   • Cornelius Vanderbilt's route connecting New York with Albany, Buffalo, and Chicago
   • James J. Hill's Great Northern from Duluth to Tacoma
   • Northern Pacific from Duluth to Tacoma
   • Union Pacific from Omaha to Promontory Point
   • Central Pacific from San Francisco to Promontory Point
   • Atchison, Topeka, and Santa Fe from St. Joseph to Los Angeles
   • Southern Pacific from New Orleans to Los Angeles
   • the extensions from Chicago to Duluth, Omaha, St. Joseph, and New Orleans

4. Draw these figures at the appropriate places:

 Promontory Point *p. 393*   Irish port of entry *p. 390*

 Ellis Island *p. 390*   port of entry to the Midwest *p. 390*

 Mesabi Range (Minn.) *p. 388*   Chinese port of entry (Calif.) *p. 391*

 Northwest forest *p. 389*

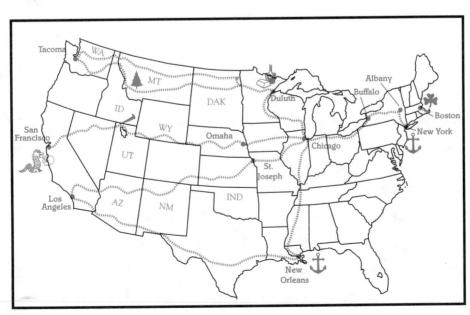

American Republic

Trivia Game: Railroads

Except for the bonus questions, you can find the answers to these trivia questions in the book. Some are harder than others. Use the index starting on page 650 in your text to help you.

Five Points

1. What is the business practice of combining small rail lines? _consolidation   p. 393_

2. Who consolidated a railroad empire from New York to the Great Lakes? _Vanderbilt   p. 393_

3. In what year was the first transcontinental railroad completed? _1869   p. 393_

4. Which line of the first transcontinental railroad crossed the Sierra Nevada? _Central Pacific   p. 394_

5. Which line of the first transcontinental railroad used Irish laborers? _Union Pacific   p. 393_

6. Where did the two lines of the first transcontinental railroad meet? _Promontory Point, Utah   p. 393_

7. What 1862 law helped settlers buy cheap land beside western railroads? _Homestead Act   p. 394_

8. Who built the Great Northern Railroad? _James J. Hill   p. 395_

9. What is America's first major act regulating business? _Interstate Commerce Act   p. 400_

10. What did the Interstate Commerce Commission regulate? _railroad rates   p. 400_

Ten Points

11. Who was the first American to make a major trial of a railroad (1830)? _Peter Cooper   p. 262_

12. What locomotive lost a famous race with a stagecoach outside Baltimore? _Tom Thumb   p. 265_

13. What was the first locomotive to pull a train of cars in regular service? _Best Friend   p. 263_

14. Where was the longest railroad in the world in the early 1830s? _Charleston to Hamburg, S.C. p. 263_

15. What land did the U.S. buy from Mexico to build a southern transcontinental railroad?
Gadsden Purchase   pp. 299-300

16. What was the first war to rely on railroads to transport troops? _Civil War   p. 338_

17. What animals, used by the Plains Indians, did railroad crews slaughter for sport? _buffalo   p. 409_

18. What animals did cowboys drive from Texas to the railroads in Kansas? _cattle   pp. 413-14_

19. During what war did the U.S. government take control of all railroads? _World War I   p. 483_

Bonus Questions (Fifteen Points)

20. Who invented the air brake in 1869? _George Westinghouse_

21. What standard gauge of track did U.S. railroads finally adopt in 1886? _4' 8.5"_

22. How many transcontinental railroads did the U.S. have in 1900? _five_

23. What country has the most miles of railroad track in the world? _United States_

American Republic

Ways of Doing Business   ☆ *Classroom discussion*

Complete the chart. For each type of business, write a definition, an example, its advantages, and its disadvantages.

Type	Definition	Example	Advantages	Disadvantages
Sole Proprietorship *p. 396*	a business with one owner	Edison's Menlo Park Lab	Owner is free to make decisions. Owner receives all profits.	Owner absorbs all losses. Owner's capital is limited.
Partnership *p. 396*	a business with two or more owners	Carnegie's steel empire	More capital is available. Partners share losses. Partners share expertise.	Partners share losses regardless of responsibility. All partners must participate in deals. Partnerships can dissolve easily.
Corporation *pp. 396-97*	a business with ownership by stockholders	Bell Telephone Company	Large capital is available. Losses are limited to investments. Stockholders need not participate in deals. Death does not dissolve the business.	loss of individual control and large profits by one owner
Trust *pp. 397, 401*	combination of several companies into a giant corporation managed by trust executives	Rockefeller's Standard Oil	Executives can manage many related companies efficiently.	Trusts gain advantages that can harm free enterprise.
Holding Company *p. 401*	company that controls other companies by buying stock	James Hill's Northern Securities	Antitrust laws are avoided because member firms keep their names. Member firms are managed efficiently.	Holding companies also limit free enterprise.

American Republic

Chapter 20   Activity A

It's the End of the Trail for the Great American Cattle Drive

You have discovered an old newspaper account describing the end of the cattle drive. But it has twenty-five mistakes! Sometimes words are misspelled; other times the wrong word has been used. Underline the mistakes and write the correct word above each mistake.

Reporter: Jake Slim   Place: San Antonio, Texas   Date: April 7, 1896

The cattle drive symbolizes America's tough frontier spirit. Ever since the end of the

Civil p. 411   *longhorn p. 413*
Mexican War, Texas cattlemen have battled against impossible odds to ship their loghorn cattle to

                                        Sedalia p. 413
hungry Easterners. The first cattle drives stopped in Kansas City, Missouri. But angry farmers

                                Abilene p. 414   *Chisholm p. 414*
forced the cowboys to open a new route in 1867 to Abiline, Kansas. Although the Chizolm Trail

                                Chickasaw p. 414
saved time, the cowboys met resistance from the Chikasaw Indians. So new trails were opened

              Ellsworth p. 414
farther west to Ellesworth and Dodge City. The most daring trail of all was the Goodnight-

Loving p. 415   *Pecos p. 415*
Cheyenne Trail, which followed the Red River and then cut across eighty miles of waterless

       Comanche p. 415   *Loving p. 415*
plains. Nez Perce Indians often attacked cowboys on this trail, and they even killed Goodnight on

one of his drives.

                                                        spring p. 415
The cattle drive is something to see! Preparation for the trail drive begins in early fall when

the rancher gathers up his herd. The typical crew consists of a cook, two point men, two swing

                                 boss p. 415   wrangler p. 416   boss p. 415
men, two flank men, two drag men, a trail hoss, and a straggler. The trail hoss is in charge of the

               wrangler p. 416
men and animals, and the straggler takes care of the horses and equipment. Cowboys ride all day

and enjoy little sleep at night. The cowboys battle Indians, hail, fire, dust, disease, loneliness, and

drought p. 417   frightening p. 416   *stampede p. 416*
drowt. But the most frightning experience of all is the stampeede.

      The cowboys fear that the great American cattle drive will soon be over. Many ranchers went

              drought p. 417   *blizzard p. 417*
broke after the drowt in the summer of 1884 and the deadly blizard that followed. The ranchers

                                    drought p. 417
who survived say that another bad winter or drowt will ruin them too. They also blame the meat

             Armour p. 416   *woollybacks p. 418*
packer Philip Armor and the invasion of the woolybacks. The ranchers are begging President

Cleveland p. 417
Clevland to send aid because the losses are more than they can bear.

American Republic

Outlining Paragraphs

Every paragraph in your text fits into an outline, even if the paragraph does not have a heading. Look at the topic sentences in your textbook to complete this outline for "Overcoming the Obstacles to Settlement" (pp. 421-24). The answers are listed at the bottom.

I. Overcoming the Obstacles to Settlement

    A. A Lack of Some Resources

        1. _Rarity of Trees_

            a. _Lack of Wood for Log Cabins_   _sod house_

            b. _Lack of Wood for Fuel_

            c. _Lack of Wood for Split Rail Fences_

        2. _Inadequate Water Supply_   _windmill_

    B. Help for the Prairie Farmers

        1. _Barbed Wire_   _Glidden_

        2. _Halladay Windmill_

        3. _Railroads_

        4. _American Ingenuity_

    C. Hardships of the Prairie Settler

        1. _Erosion of Topsoil_

        2. _Prairie Fire_

        3. _Storms_

        4. _Swarms of Locusts and Grasshoppers_

        5. _Loneliness_   _RFD; Grange_

Swarms of Locusts and Grasshoppers	Barbed Wire
Lack of Wood for Fuel	Prairie Fire
Inadequate Water Supply	American Ingenuity
Lack of Wood for Split Rail Fences	Rarity of Trees
Halladay Windmill	Railroads
Lack of Wood for Log Cabins	Loneliness
Erosion of Topsoil	Storms

Now write these terms beside the point in the outline where they are discussed: sod house, windmill, Glidden, RFD, Grange.

American Republic

Chapter 20   Activity C

Trivia Game: Indians

Except for the bonus questions, you can find the answers to these trivia questions in the book. Some are harder than others. Use the index starting on page 650 of your text to help you.

Five Points

1. What type of Indians lived between the Mississippi and the Rockies? _Plains Indians   p. 409_

2. What modern state was once Indian Territory? _Oklahoma   p. 420_

3. Upon what animal of the American West did the nomadic Indians depend? _buffalo   p. 409_

4. What do we call tracts of land set aside for Indians? _reservations   p. 425_

5. What U.S. officer lost his army at the Battle of Little Big Horn? _Custer   p. 424_

6. Name one Sioux chief who fought at the Battle of Little Big Horn. _Crazy Horse or Gall   p. 424_

7. What medicine man inspired the Sioux at the Battle of Little Big Horn? _Sitting Bull   p. 424_

8. What Nez Perce chief tried to flee to Canada but was captured? _Joseph   p. 425_

9. What term describes Indians placed under federal protection and support? _wards   p. 426_

10. What act in 1887 tried to assimilate the Indians into mainstream America? _Dawes Act   p. 426_

11. Name a famous Apache warrior. _Geronimo   p. 425_

12. In what year did the U.S. set up a policy of Indian self-determination? _1970   p. 427_

13. What term describes Indians who are constantly moving in search of food? _nomadic   pp. 2, 409_

14. What civilized Indians did Andrew Jackson forcibly remove from Georgia in the 1830s after gold was discovered on their land? _Cherokee   p. 237_

Ten Points

15. Who first called the native Americans *Indians?* _Columbus   p. 1_

16. What ancient Indian civilization flourished on the Yucatán Peninsula in Mexico? _Maya   p. 2_

17. What fierce Indian warriors built a civilization on Lake Texcoco in Mexico? _Aztec   p. 3_

18. What road-building Indians lived in the land that is modern-day Peru? _Inca   p. 3_

19. What Indian taught the Plymouth colonists how to plant corn? _Squanto   p. 19_

20. What antiwar religious group from Germany converted many Indians? _Moravians   p. 55_

21. What Indian confederation joined the British in the French and Indian War? _Iroquois   p. 75_

22. What Ottawa chief organized the frontier tribes to stop colonial settlement? _Pontiac   p. 80_

23. During what victory did Anthony Wayne win control of half of Ohio? _Fallen Timbers   p. 175_

24. What Shoshone woman aided Lewis and Clark's western expedition? _Sacajawea   p. 200_

25. What Shawnee chief created an Indian Confederation based at Prophetstown? _Tecumseh   pp. 206-7_

26. Who beat the Creeks at Horseshoe Bend, opening the Deep South to settlers? _A. Jackson_ _p. 220_

27. What Indian scholar developed a Cherokee alphabet? _Sequoyah_ _p. 238_

28. What leader of the Sauk and Fox tribes led a hopeless rebellion in 1832 that ended with the death of almost all his followers at the Bad Axe Massacre? _Black Hawk_ _p. 238_

Fifteen Points

29. What Dutch leader bought Manhattan Island from the Indians? _Peter Minuit_ _p. 25_

30. What tribe enjoyed a "Golden Age of Indian Work" under Zeisberger? _Delaware_ _p. 56_

31. What missionary from the Great Awakening died of tuberculosis at age twenty-nine? _David Brainerd_ _p. 60_

32. What college was founded in 1770 to train missionaries to the Indians? _Dartmouth_ _p. 60_

33. What Mohawk chieftain translated Mark's gospel into Mohawk? _Joseph Brant_ _p. 104_

34. Where does the Constitution treat Indian tribes as independent nations? _Article 1, Section 8_ _p. 142_

35. What president won fame for his victory at the Tippecanoe River? _W. H. Harrison_ _pp. 206-7_

36. What former president said in 1837 of America's Indian policy, "These are crying sins for which we are answerable before a higher jurisdiction"? _John Quincy Adams_ _p. 238_

37. What colonial road followed the Great Warrior's Path? _Great Wagon Road_ _p. 256_

38. What valuable liquid was discovered under "undesirable" Indian reservations? _oil_ _p. 426_

Bonus Questions (Twenty Points)

39. What Indian "princess" did Virginia settler John Rolfe marry? _Pocahontas_ _p. 28_

40. What war in 1637 cleared the Connecticut Valley of Indians? _Pequot War_

41. Which type of Indians wore long war bonnets made from eagles' feathers? _Sioux_

42. What do we call the leather shoes worn by the Indians? _moccasins_

43. What do we call the dome-shaped framed houses of the Woodland Indians? _wigwams_

44. What are the cone-shaped tents of the Plains Indians called? _tepees_

45. Name one common European disease that killed many Indians. _smallpox_

46. What type of tall posts did the Indians of the Northwest coast carve? _totem poles_

47. What were the frames called that Indians attached to dogs to carry packs? _travois_

48. What did Indians call the feat of touching enemies during battle? _counting coups_

49. What massacre marks the final defeat of the Indians in 1890? _Wounded Knee_ _p. 426_

50. When did Congress grant all Indians American citizenship? _1924_

American Republic

People of the Last Frontier

Match these people with the comments you would expect them to make.

A. miner	C. homesteader
B. cowboy	D. Indian

__A__ 1. I wish I could find my own Comstock Lode! *p. 410*

__D__ 2. The United States Cavalry attacked our camp yesterday, killing many of my brothers. *p. 424*

__C__ 3. I just bought a hundred-pound roll of Glidden's miracle "yarn." *p. 422*

__D__ 4. Many of my friends have been going to the Ghost Dance. *p. 425*

__A__ 5. My next stop will probably be the Black Hills of South Dakota. *p. 410*

__B__ 6. We spent a rowdy night in Abilene after our trip was over! *p. 414*

__B__ 7. My trail boss is considered the best in the business. *p. 415*

__C__ 8. In my opinion, our sod house is no better than a hole in the ground. *p. 421*

__C__ 9. Everyone is joining the Grange, which promises us a better life. *p. 424*

__A__ 10. "Pike's Peak or bust!" is my dream. *p. 409*

__C__ 11. The Sooners took the best locations before I got here. *p. 420*

__C__ 12. We recently installed a Halladay windmill, hoping it will make our work easier. *p. 422*

__D__ 13. The missionaries are our best friends, even though they are white. *p. 426*

__A__ 14. The buildings in town were just thrown together; soon it will be a ghost town. *pp. 410-11*

__B__ 15. We had a difficult time during our trip up the Sedalia Trail. *p. 413*

__C__ 16. The post office has finally installed rural free delivery in our area! *p. 424*

__D__ 17. The Dawes Act has assigned only 160 acres to each father. *p. 426*

__B__ 18. The deadly blizzard of '84 has caused widespread bankruptcy. *p. 417*

__D__ 19. I do not believe my extended family can survive on the reservation. *p. 425*

__C__ 20. We thought the drought was bad enough, until the locusts came! *p. 423*

__D__ 21. It seems that alcohol is the only thing left to help us forget our defeat. *p. 426*

__D__ 22. We have decided to give up and become wards of the state. *p. 426*

__B__ 23. We all look up to Charles Goodnight as the noblest example of our kind. *p. 415*

__C__ 24. The most exciting mail we receive each year is the mail-order catalog from Wards. *p. 424*

__B__ 25. Nothing arouses my anger more than the sight of a woollyback. *p. 418*

__B__ 26. My first job will be as a wrangler. *p. 416*

__B__ 27. Refrigerator cars have greatly benefited our industry. *p. 417*

__A__ 28. Guidebooks suggest that we should form four-man companies to economize expenses. *p. 410*

__B__ 29. Our byproducts supply the East with soap, glue, buttons, and fertilizer. *p. 417*

American Republic

Case #4: Taming the West

Sir Vey has been called upon by the GIA to solve another case. Two outlaws of the West are breaking into food stores and filling their bellies full of honey and tin cans. GIA agents have identified the two as Black Bear Bart and his young goat friend, Billy the Kid. Lawman Bat Masterson has found a short and poorly written poem at each crime scene—the trademark of Black Bear Bart. Each poem reveals something about the next targeted city. Now it's up to Sir Vey to read the poem clues, track down the criminals, and bring order to the West. Use the maps and text from Chapters 19 and 20 and the map of the West on page 431 to help Sir Vey solve the case.

1. We'll head to the city in Nevada

   That the Humboldt River flows in and outta. ___Elko   p. 431___

2. The next place we're planning to go

   Is the capital of New Mexico. ___Santa Fe   p. 431___

3. The Central Pacific railroad will keep us in motion

   Until we reach the city on the Pacific Ocean. ___San Francisco   p. 395___

4. If you're a-wanting to lock us up in jail,

   Find the city at the northern end of the Goodnight-Loving Trail. ___Cheyenne   p. 414___

5. Heading for Nevada I am,

   To the city closest to Hoover Dam. ___Las Vegas   p. 431___

6. Can't catch us? What a pity!

   Try heading to the state capital near Virginia City. ___Carson City   pp. 410, 431___

7. To Wyoming, Kid and I will ride,

   To the city west of the Continental Divide. _Jackson   p. 431_

8. On our way to a city in Utah we're headed,

   Very close to where Union Pacific and Central Pacific were wedded. _Ogden   p. 393_

9. One hundred fifty miles from Grand Coulee Dam we'll go.

   We'll get the food we want in Idaho. _Lewiston   p. 431_

10. In New Mexico more than one city on the Rio Grande you'll find,

    But the southernmost one is where we'll dine. _Las Cruces   p. 431_

11. We're in a city at a longitude of almost one hundred twenty degrees west.

    It's between the Sierra Nevada and Coast Ranges, snug as a bird in a nest. _Fresno   p. 431_

12. If you head to the state capital by Puget Sound,

    You'll quickly find that we've been around. _Olympia   p. 431_

13. We're riding hard towards the gold mines of South Pass, Wyoming.

    In the major city closest to there we'll be roaming. _Lander   pp. 410, 431_

14. If you're searching for the city we're in, Sir Vey,

    Look in Arizona on the path of the Atlantic and Pacific railway. _Flagstaff   pp. 395, 431_

15. In our quest for food we'll face heat and cold

    Until we reach the state capital near Placerville's gold. _Boise   pp. 410, 431_

16. Follow the path the Gila River flows.

    When you reach the border you'll find your foes. _Yuma   p. 431_

17. Head to the city in Colorado that nears the winding way

    Of the railroad called the Atchison, Topeka, & Santa Fe. _Pueblo   pp. 395, 431_

18. Between San Francisco and Monterey,

    You'll find the city where we plan to stay. _San Jose   p. 431_

19. The capital by the largest lake in the West

    Is the place where we're going to get food and rest. _Salt Lake City   p. 431_

20. From Glen Canyon Dam you go east on the land

    Around three hundred kilometers to our final stand. _Durango   p. 431_

American Republic

Chapter 21   Activity A

American Imperialism   *Classroom discussion*

For each foreign territory, give the nature of America's involvement (financial, diplomatic, or military); the president involved; and a major consequence of America's involvement (a benefit or problem).

	Territory	Date	Involvement	President	Consequence
Early Gains	Alaska p. 434	1867	*financial (purchase from Russia)*	*Johnson*	*valuable source of gold, oil, fish*
	Hawaii p. 435	1898	*diplomatic (annexation after Americans illegally removed the queen)*	*McKinley*	*source of pineapple and sugar cane*
Spanish-American War	Cuba pp. 438-41	1898	*military (capture of Santiago and defeat of the Spanish fleet)*	*McKinley*	*base at Guantanamo Bay; U.S. oversight of a new government; aid to the people*
	Puerto Rico pp. 440-41	1898	*military (capture of the island without resistance)*	*McKinley*	*U.S. establishment of a territory/commonwealth; aid and economic benefits to the people*
	Philippines pp. 440-42	1898	*military (defeat of the Spanish fleet at Manila Bay)*	*McKinley*	*base for trade with China; costly war with Aguinaldo; U.S. oversight of independence; aid to the people*
Latin America	Venezuela pp. 444-45	1902	*diplomatic (prevention of a European attack to collect unpaid loans)*	*Roosevelt*	*issue of the Roosevelt Corollary, which began sixty years of U.S. military intervention*
	Panama p. 443-44	1903	*military (support of a revolt against Colombia)*	*Roosevelt*	*construction of the Panama Canal*
Asia	China p. 446	1899, 1900	*diplomatic (circulation of the Open Door Policy); military (defeat of the Boxer Rebellion)*	*McKinley*	*protection of Chinese land; missions; education of Chinese in the U.S.; Chinese and U.S. friendship*
	Japan pp. 446-47	1853	*diplomatic (opening of trade)*	*Fillmore*	*rapid development of Japan's modern military power; Japanese victories against China and Russia*
	p. 447	1905	*diplomatic (Portsmouth treaty between Japan and Russia)*	*Roosevelt*	*maintenance of Asia's balance of power; Roosevelt's Nobel Peace Prize*

American Republic

The Five *W*s

Good reporters attempt to answer five basic questions: Who? What? Where? When? Why? List the facts that a good newspaper should include in these reports.

Spanish Minister Blasts the President

Who? _*Dupuy de Lôme, William McKinley   p. 436*_

What? _*In a personal letter that was leaked to the press, the Spanish minister to the U.S.*_

*insulted the president by calling him a weak crowd pleaser and "common politician."*

Where? _*Washington, D.C.*_

When? _*February 1898*_

Why? _*Spain feared that the president might give in to public pressure to intervene in Cuba.*_

American Warship Blows Up

Who? _*American officers and enlisted men, suspected conspirators   p. 436*_

What? _*During a goodwill mission to Cuba, the U.S.S. Maine blew up, killing two officers and*_

*250 enlisted men.*

Where? _*Havana, Cuba*_

When? _*February 15, 1898*_

Why? _*Although Spain was blamed for the mysterious explosion, there were many*_

*possible explanations.*

President Declares War

Who? _*William McKinley, Congress   p. 438*_

What? _*Congress declared war on Spain.*_

Where? _*Washington, D.C.*_

When? _*April 25, 1898*_

Why? _*When the United States decided to recognize Cuba's independence, Spain declared*_

*war to uphold its honor.*

Spain's Pacific Fleet Destroyed

Who? _Commodore George Dewey, the Pacific fleets of America and Spain   pp. 439-40_

What? _In a brief battle the American fleet destroyed most of the Spanish fleet, killing 167_

Spaniards without losing a single American in combat.

Where? _Manila Bay, Philippines_

When? _May 1, 1898_

Why? _Long before war was declared, Dewey had been told to plan an attack. The Spanish_

were obviously not as prepared as he was.

Treaty Ends War with Spain

Who? _Spanish and American treaty commissioners   pp. 440-42_

What? _Spain signed the Treaty of Paris, agreeing to give up its claim to Cuba and to cede_

Guam, the Philippines, and Puerto Rico to the U.S. in return for $20 million.

Where? _Paris_

When? _December 10, 1898_

Why? _America, the victor in the war, desired to fulfill its imperialist dreams with the islands it_

had captured. (The Teller Amendment prevented America from annexing Cuba as well.)

America Signs Treaty with Panama

Who? _Secretary of State John Hay, Philippe Bunau-Varilla   pp. 443-44_

What? _America and Panama signed the Hay-Bunau-Varilla Treaty granting the U.S. perpetual_

use of a "canal zone." The canal will be open to all nations on equal terms.

Where? _Washington, D.C._

When? _November 18, 1903_

Why? _The U.S. had encouraged and supported Panama's revolt so that America could buy_

rights for a canal.

American Republic

Spanish-American War: Causes and Consequences

The Spanish-American War marked a turning point in America's foreign relations. Such a fundamental change had many complex causes and consequences. In the exercise below, write the number of each fact in the correct blank.

A. Causes of the War ___*3, 6, 8, 11, 12, 17, 18*_____

B. Events During the War ___*1, 7, 13*_____

C. Consequences of the War ___*2, 4, 5, 9, 10, 14, 15, 16*_____

1. The Rough Riders, led by Theodore Roosevelt, charged up San Juan Hill and helped to capture Santiago.

2. Emilio Aguinaldo fought for two and one-half years against the United States.

3. Hearst's *New York Journal* published an insulting letter by Dupuy de Lôme.

4. The U.S. Navy opened a base at Guantanamo Bay, Cuba.

5. William Gorgas drained Cuba's mosquito-infested swamps.

6. Revolutionaries in Cuba attempted to destroy the island's livelihood (the sugar industry).

7. Commodore Dewey crushed the Spanish fleet at Manila Bay, Philippines.

8. The U.S.S. *Maine* blew up in Havana, Cuba.

9. The Platt amendment strictly regulated Cuba's government.

10. As a provision of the Treaty of Paris, the U.S. paid Spain $20 million for taking Spain's possessions.

11. Joseph Pulitzer's yellow journalism in the *New York World* fed Americans a steady diet of Spanish oppression in Cuba.

12. American investors in Cuba frantically pressured President McKinley to protect their investments from terrorists.

13. The American army captured Puerto Rico without resistance.

14. The United States sent millions of dollars in aid to the Philippines.

15. The United States carefully controlled the development of the governments in Cuba, Puerto Rico, and the Philippines.

16. Anti-imperialists in the Senate hotly debated America's plans to violate the Monroe Doctrine, but the imperialists won.

17. Spain made no efforts to improve harsh conditions in Cuba.

18. European nations began competing with one another to extend their military power and colonial empires.

American Republic

Chapter 22   Activity A

Finding the Foremost Facts About Changing American Life

For each characteristic of American life listed below, give what you think is the best example of the changes that were occurring at the end of the 1800s.

People

1. population ___*The population reached seventy-five million, growing by over a million a year.*___ *pp. 452-53*

2. urbanization ___*By 1920 more than one-half of all Americans lived in towns and cities.*___ *p. 453*

Opportunities

3. secondary schools ___*Free secondary schools increased from one hundred in 1860 to twelve thousand in 1915.*___ *p. 453*

4. higher education ___*More options were open to all people, including blacks and women.*___ *pp. 453-54*

5. middle class ___*Many poor Americans were able to join the ranks of the middle class.*___ *pp. 454-55*

Leisure

6. working conditions ___*By 1910 the average work week had dropped from about 70 to 54.6 hours.*___ *p. 455*

7. spectator sports ___*Many people participated in new American spectator sports, particularly baseball.*___ *p. 455*

8. literature ___*More people began to read books, especially the American books of Mark Twain.*___ *p. 455*

Values

9. new religious groups ___*Immigrants increased Lutheranism, rationalism, and Catholicism; cults started.*___ *p. 456*

10. religious liberalism ___*Ministers questioned the Bible and emphasized the social gospel.*___ *pp. 456-57*

11. humanitarianism ___*Temperance societies and interdenominational organizations, such as the YMCA, arose.*___ *pp. 457-59*

Map Study: New States

Label these new states with their abbreviations: Kans. (1861); W.Va. (1863); Nev. (1864); Nebr. (1867); Colo. (1876); Wash., Mont., N.Dak., S.Dak. (1889); Idaho, Wyo. (1890); Utah (1896); Okla. (1907); Ariz., N.Mex. (1912).

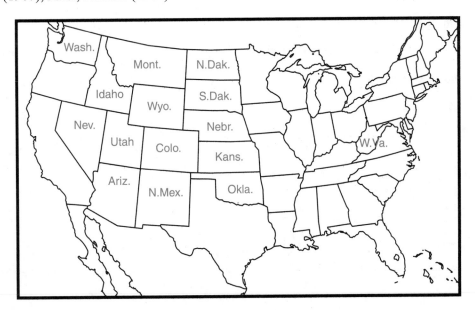

American Republic

Progressivism

Complete this summary of the Progressive Era using your text, pages 459-62. The summary about progressive aims is done for you. Write three short paragraphs on the other three sections about uncovering corruption, revealing society's ills, and reforms. Remember to look at the topic sentences. Include these terms in your paragraphs:

"Boss" Tweed   recall   referendum
civil service   initiative   Amendment Seventeen

The progressives looked to government for the answers to America's problems. Progressives had three aims. First, they sought to abolish corruption and unfair practices. Second, they sought to give people more say in governing. Third, they believed that government should improve society.

Progressives sought to correct corruption in government and industry through reform. They attacked city corruption (such as that of "Boss" Tweed in New York City), state corruption, and national corruption. They replaced the spoils system with the civil service. They also attacked unfair business practices and poor labor conditions.

Progressives sought to improve living conditions in the crowded cities. Families lived in poor housing. Poor sanitation made epidemics common. Many homes lacked sufficient water and plumbing. Housing was even worse for people confined to other institutions, such as prisons and mental hospitals.

Progressives introduced new reforms. Some cities hired a city manager or commissioners. Many states allowed the people to petition for change through recall of elected officials, initiative of new laws, and referendum of unpopular laws. Amendment Seventeen let people elect senators directly. Some individuals started settlement houses, such as Jane Addams's Hull House. Others worked to improve prisons and mental institutions.

American Republic

The Progressive Presidents

Complete the chart.

	Theodore Roosevelt	**William Howard Taft**	**Woodrow Wilson**
Years in Office	1901-1909 p. 463	1909-1913 p. 466	1913-1921 p. 468
Political Party	Republican p. 463	Republican p. 466	Democrat p. 468
Occupation	historian, rancher p. 463	lawyer p. 466	lawyer, teacher p. 468
Home	Sagamore Hill, N.Y. p. 463	Cincinnati, Ohio p. 466	Washington, D.C. p. 468
Religion	Dutch Reformed p. 463	Unitarian p. 466	Presbyterian p. 468
Foreign Policy	"big stick"	"dollar diplomacy"	"moral diplomacy"
Domestic Policy	"a square deal" p. 464	no slogan	"New Freedom" p. 466
Approach Toward Big Business	Government should control big business and promote better working conditions. pp. 464-65	same as Roosevelt, but more easygoing p. 465	Rather than regulating trusts, he wanted to break them up into small companies. p. 467
Major Laws/ Amendments	Pure Food and Drug Act; New Lands Act p. 464	Sixteenth Amendment; Seventeenth Amendment; Payne-Aldrich Tariff p. 465	Clayton Anti-Trust Act; Underwood Tariff of 1913 [Eighteenth Amendment; Nineteenth Amendment] p. 467
Progressive Reforms	intervention in strikes; forest reserve system; forty-three antitrust suits pp. 464-65	Department of Labor; Children's Bureau; eighty-nine antitrust suits p. 465	Federal Trade Commission; Federal Reserve System p. 467-68
Presidential "Firsts"	first to travel outside U.S.; first to fly in an airplane; Nobel Peace Prize p. 463	first to open baseball season; heaviest president; first with an official automobile; first to be buried at Arlington p. 466	first with earned Ph.D. p. 468

American Republic

Chapter 22   Activity D

Find the Message

Beside each phrase write the person, term, or event that it describes. Then transfer the letters to the appropriate blanks below to find what Teddy Roosevelt said about "New Nationalism."

1. George W. Carver's useful root

P E A N U T   p. 454
39   17 1

2. cult founded by Charles Russell

J E H O V A H'S
6   10   37

W I T N E S S E S   p. 456
36

3. author of *Origin of Species*

D A R W I N   p. 457
27 22

4. "prohibition" amendment

E I G H T E E N T H   p. 469
3   12   38   25

5. corrupt New York City "boss"

T W E E D   p. 460
21   7

6. journalist who exposes society's ills

M U C K R A K E R   p. 461
18   32   26

7. author of *The Jungle*

S I N C L A I R   p. 461
23   31

8. voters' petition to remove an official

R E C A L L   p. 462
16   29

9. voters' petition to stop legislation

R E F E R E N D U M   p. 462
30   40

10. voters' petition to pass legislation

I N I T I A T I V E   p. 462
20   9   15

11. Roosevelt's chief forester

P I N C H O T   p. 464
42   2 13

12. subject of the Sixteenth Amendment

I N C O M E   T A X   p. 465
34 33   24

13. Republican nominee in 1912

T A F T   p. 465
35

14. Roosevelt's Progressive Party

B U L L   M O O S E   p. 466
5   43   4   44

15. sponsor of the Anti-Trust Act of 1914

C L A Y T O N   p. 467
8   41

16. Wilson's progressive banking system

F E D E R A L   R E S E R V E   p. 468
11 19   28   14

T H E   O B J E C T   O F   G O V E R N M E N T
1 2 3   4 5 6 7 8 9   10 11   12 13 14 15 16 17 18 19 20 21

I S   T H E   W E L F A R E   O F   T H E
22 23   24 25 26   27 28 29 30 31 32 33   34 35   36 37 38

P E O P L E .
39 40 41 42 43 44

American Republic

Experiences of War ☆ *Classroom discussion*

Americans' experience in the Great War differed radically from the Europeans' experience. Complete the chart showing the major differences between the United States and France.

		France	United States
Background	**Reasons for War**	nationalism; imperialism; militarism; alliances p. 476	sentiment for Allies; trade with Allies; Allied propaganda; unrestricted submarine warfare pp. 479-80
	Prewar Alliances	Triple Entente p. 476	none (neutrality) p. 476
	Sparks of War	assassination of Archduke Ferdinand; German declaration of war on Russia pp. 475-77	resumption of unrestricted submarine warfare; Zimmermann telegram pp. 480-81
Preparations	**Year of Entry**	1914	1917
	Preparedness for War	large and powerful military p. 476	small army; few heavy guns; no tanks; no air force p. 482
	Original Size of Army	4,017,000	200,000 p. 482
	Total Forces in Army	8,410,000	4,000,000 p. 482
	Sources of Money	loans from United States p. 486	income and corporate taxes; bank loans and loan drives p. 486
Fighting	**Commanding General**	Ferdinand Foch p. 487	John Pershing p. 487
	Success of Early Battles	a bloody stalemate in the trenches p. 477	a string of quick, bloody victories pp. 488-89
	Total Years at War	5 p. 490	1 1/2 p. 490
	Total Deaths	1,357,800	115,000 p. 490
	Total Wounded	4,266,000	200,000 p. 490
Peace	**Political Leader**	Georges Clemenceau p. 491	Woodrow Wilson p. 490
	Aims for Peace	insurance that Germany would never again be strong p. 491	"peace without victory" (Fourteen Points); League of Nations; generous terms; no territorial gains or reparations p. 490
	Benefits from the Treaty of Versailles	blame for war laid on Germany; huge reparations from Germany; control of German empire and land p. 491	none (never ratified by the Senate) p. 492
	Participation in the League of Nations	major, active participant	none (never joined) p. 492

American Republic

Chapter 23   Activity B

What God Says About War and Peace

In his war message to Congress, President Wilson rallied Americans behind the war by appealing to their sense of justice and their dreams of a lasting peace. Use your Bible to find what God says about man's violence, just wars, and man's hope for peace.

1. Mankind has suffered from violence since the beginning of time. Wilson explained his outrage at the unrestricted killing of innocent men, women, and children: "The present German submarine warfare against commerce is a warfare against mankind."

   • When was the world first filled with violence (Gen. 6:10-13)? __Noah's generation__

   • What caused the war mentioned in Genesis 14:1-10? __rebellion__

   • What does the victor of a war normally seek (Gen. 14:11-12)? __spoils__

   • What does Jesus warn about relying on violence (Matt. 26:52)? __leads to death__

   • What is the source of quarrels, even among Christians (James 4:1-3)? __lusts__

   • Who started the first "war" (Rev. 12:7-9)? __Satan__

2. Wilson believed in "just" war. He said about America's entry into World War I, "We have no selfish ends to serve. We desire no conquest, no dominion. We seek no indemnities for ourselves, no material compensation for the sacrifices we shall freely make. We are but one of the champions of the rights of mankind."

   • Why did Abram go to war (Gen. 14:14-16)? __to save Lot__

   • After Abram's slaughter, why did the priest praise God (Gen. 14:17-20)? __victory__

   • What did Abram do with his spoils of war (Gen. 14:21-24)? __didn't accept any__

   • Why do heathen nations want rulers (I Sam. 8:19-20)? __justice and war__

   • Does God use imperfect nations to fight His wars (Deut. 9:1-6)? __yes__

   • Why did God want all the Canaanites to die (Deut. 20:16-18)? __abominations__

   • What did God promise if Israel became wicked (Lev. 18:24-30)? __expulsion__

3. Mankind has never enjoyed lasting peace. Yet Wilson wanted Americans "to fight for the ultimate peace of the world and for the liberation of its peoples, the German peoples included."

   • Did God instruct Israel to "liberate" its foreign enemies (Deut. 20:10-15)? __no__

   • What two things have an equal place in God's plan (Eccles. 3:1, 8)? __war and peace__

   • What does Jesus say we should expect in the end times (Matt. 24:6)? __wars__

   • Where does Jesus say we can find lasting peace (John 14:27)? __Jesus__

   • Who alone has the power to stop the fighting among nations (Isa. 2:1-4)? __God__

   • Who will fight the last war to end all wars (Rev. 19:11-21)? __Jesus__

American Republic

War Diaries

One interesting source of information about World War I is the many diaries. Create diary entries for an imaginary American couple. Pretend that the husband is one of the first eager doughboys in the 2nd Division, who is training in the Verdun trenches before any major fighting. His young wife is doing everything she can to support the war effort at home. (Include at least three of the terms below each diary entry in your entry.)

Husband's Diary   *Answers will vary.*

Name _Richard Lee Cooper_____   Age _21_____

Rank _private_____   Specialty _scout_____

Date _8 February 1918_____   Entry _Miss Jackie and Jimmy terribly. Weather cold, but

at least the lice are gone. Frogs still in the dumps about the war. Argue with us about

Fourteen Points, but what do they know? Frog commanders too uppity for me, but there

are rumors that Pershing's demanding that we have our own independent army. All of us

eager for the spring, but uncertain about new operations. Scouting not too dangerous,

for now. Shot at last night. Say my prayers every day. Company desperately short of

heavy guns and tanks. Drilled for mustard gas again, but still none of the real stuff. Saw

my first dogfight yesterday. Our boys took a beating. Thirty planes downed. Looks like my

buddy Jack got influenza. Let's clean up the Huns and get out of here! Miss Jackie.

trench   barbed wire   tank   mustard gas   dogfight   influenza   Pershing   Fourteen Points

Wife's Diary   *Answers will vary.*

Name _Jacqueline Haley Cooper_____   Age _21_____   Children _1_____

Hometown _Lancaster, Pennsylvania_____   Occupation _housewife_____

Date _8 February 1918_____   Entry _Got a letter from Rick today. So far he's fine._

Jimmy can say "daddy" when I show him Rick's picture, but of course he doesn't under-

stand. Yesterday was another gasless day. I don't mind as long as it'll get our boys

home quicker. The four-minute man at the show last night brought tears to all our eyes.

Marge told me that John is shipping out next week. Hope I can encourage her. The work

for the Red Cross keeps us busy, but we can't get our minds off the war. Rick would be

proud that I have saved almost enough to get my first Liberty loan. Maybe next month I'll

have enough. Saving my thrift stamps too. Anything for Rick. The paper says that Wilson's

calling for more factory workers. Should I go? What about Jimmy? I'll do anything if it

will help Rick. I miss him.

gasless day   Victory Garden   Red Cross   four-minute man   Liberty loan   stamp day   Wilson

American Republic

Chapter 23   Activity D

Words You Need to Know: *Objectivity* and *Propaganda*

World War I introduced modern *propaganda:* "a systematic effort to manipulate other people's beliefs, attitudes, or actions by means of various symbols." Propaganda deliberately selects facts or rumors to manipulate an audience. In contrast, *objectivity* is "an honest effort to avoid appeals to emotion, conjecture, or personal prejudice." For each statement below, write whether it appears to be an example of objectivity or propaganda.

propaganda   1. The British press reports that Germany has just opened a "corpse factory" that converts human bodies into soap.

objectivity   2. Both the Allies and the Central Powers violated America's neutral rights at sea.

objectivity   3. *Lusitania* was twice torpedoed off the Irish coast by a German submarine, and probably one thousand passengers are dead.

propaganda   4. In an act of mass murder that would make a cannibal blush, a German sub sank the helpless *Lusitania,* killing all aboard.

propaganda   5. Belgian refugees have seen with their own eyes German soldiers cutting off the hands of babies.

objectivity   6. Yesterday a German firing squad shot Edith Cavell, an English nurse who had been helping Allied soldiers escape.

propaganda   7. Are we neutral when we sell acid for profit and ten thousand German graves bear the legend "Made in America"?

propaganda   8. Destroy this mad German brute. Enlist!

propaganda   9. Support the flag of liberty! Buy U.S. government bonds.

Finding Original Sources

Tell whether each of the following is a primary source or a secondary source of information about World War I. A primary source is written by people who lived through the event.

secondary source   10. an encyclopedia article on World War I

primary source   11. a newspaper from November 1918

primary source   12. letters written by a doughboy stationed in France

secondary source   13. your textbook

primary source   14. a poster advertising U.S. war bonds

secondary source   15. an atlas showing troop movements in the Argonne offensive

secondary source   16. an article in a history magazine on weapons in World War I

primary source   17. a copy of the Treaty of Versailles

secondary source   18. *The Guns of August* (a book about World War I)

primary source   19. a Renault tank (used by the French during World War I)

American Republic

Map Study: World War I

The American Expeditionary Force (A.E.F.) arrived on the Western front at a dramatic point in the war. For four bloody years both sides had fought along the same line of trenches, and both sides began to feel secure in their defenses. But Germany's all-out offensive in the spring of 1918 punched two major holes in this "wall." Many of the weary French panicked and ran. Almost nothing stood between the Germans and Paris. But Americans helped stand in the gap. Having thrown everything into the offensive, the German army had nothing left to continue. In fact, they were now spread too thin beyond the safety of their own wall.

In a rapid series of counter thrusts, the French, British, and American armies punched holes into the thin German wall. Now it was the worn-out Germans' turn to panic and run. But they had no "doughboys" to stand in the gap, and they had no new walls to run to! Their only escape and source of food, gasoline, and bullets was a railroad running along the rear through Aulnoye and Mézières. When the Allies captured these rail heads, defeat was certain. Refer to the map in the textbook on page 489 to complete the map on the next page. The trench line in late 1917 has already been drawn for you.

1. Label these countries with abbreviations: France (Fr.), Belgium (Bel.), The Netherlands (Neth.), Germany (Ger.).

2. Using a blue pencil, label these Allied-controlled towns and cities: Ypres, Soissons, Château-Thierry, Paris, Verdun.

3. Using a red pencil, label these German-controlled towns and cities: Mézières, Sedan, St. Mihiel, Luxembourg, Brussels.

4. Connect these German-controlled cities with rail lines:

   • Strasbourg-Sedan-Mézières-Aulnoye-Ypres
   • Mainz-Strasbourg
   • Coblenz-Luxembourg-Sedan
   • Cologne-Aulnoye

5. Connect Mézières and Paris with a road.

6. Using a red pencil, draw a thick arrow for the two main German advances:

   • from Mézières to Château-Thierry
   • from Aulnoye to Amiens

7. Using a blue pencil, draw a thick arrow for these Allied counterattacks:

   • from the Marne River to St. Mihiel
   • from Verdun to Mézières
   • from Amiens to Aulnoye

8. Draw these figures at the appropriate places:

  Belleau Wood   *p. 488*   first offensive of the U.S. Army   *p. 489*

  Argonne Forest   *p. 489*   Peace Conference   *p. 491*

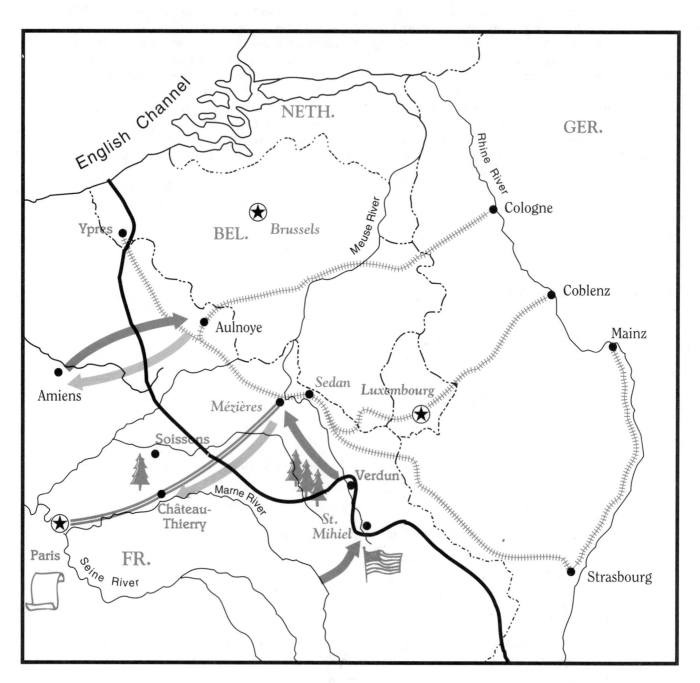

Name _____

American Republic

Chapter 23   Activity F

Write Your Own Test: Matching *Answers will vary throughout this activity.*

Write a phrase describing each person in the list. Then write the correct letter in the blank.

A. Georges Clemenceau   D. Vladimir Lenin   F. Vittorio Orlando
B. Ferdinand Foch   E. David Lloyd George   G. Arthur Zimmermann
C. Herbert Hoover

___B___ 1. *French marshal who served as Supreme Allied Commander   p. 487*

___C___ 2. *head of America's Food Administration   p. 484*

___D___ 3. *leader of the Communist Revolution in Russia   p. 488*

___G___ 4. *German foreign minister who sent an outrageous telegram to Mexico   p. 480*

___A___ 5. *French premier at the Paris Peace Conference   p. 491*

___E___ 6. *British representative at the Paris Peace Conference   p. 491*

___F___ 7. *Italian representative at the Paris Peace Conference   p. 491*

Write Your Own Test: Multiple Choice

Write four choices for each problem below. Then write the correct choice in the blank.

___C___ 8. The Central Powers included all of these countries *except*

A. *Austria-Hungary.*

B. *Germany.*

C. *Russia.   p. 477*

D. *Turkey.*

___A___ 9. To insure safe arrival in France, American ships traveled in groups called

A. *convoys.   p. 482*

B. *corps.*

C. *doughboys.*

D. *squadrons.*

___C___ 10. On what day did Germany sign an armistice?

A. *June 28, 1914*

B. *April 6, 1917*

C. *November 11, 1918   p. 490*

D. *January 18, 1919*

Write Your Own Test: Listing

Write a question for each of the lists below.

11. *Give the major reasons World War I began.*   *p. 476*
extreme nationalism, imperialism, militarism, alliances

12. *What countries formed the Triple Alliance?*   *p. 476*
Germany, Austria-Hungary, Italy

13. *What countries formed the Triple Entente?*   *p. 476*
Britain, France, Russia

14. *What countries were the main Allies?*   *p. 477*
Britain, France, Russia, Italy, United States

15. *List four warfare innovations that were introduced during World War I.*   *pp. 477-78*
tank, poison gas, airplane, grenade

16. *Name three aces from World War I.*   *p. 478*
Manfred von Richthofen, Mick Mannock, Eddie Rickenbacker

17. *Give four reasons that Americans favored the Allies.*   *pp. 479-80*
British ties, investments in Britain, Allied propaganda, unrestricted submarine warfare

18. *List five new government programs that managed the American war effort at home.*   *pp. 483-85*
War Industries Board, U.S. Railroad Administration, Fuel Administration, Food Administration, War Labor Policies Board

19. *Where were the most famous battles fought by the American Expeditionary Force?*   *pp. 488-89*
Château-Thierry, Belleau Wood, St. Mihiel, Argonne Forest

20. *Who were the Big Four at the Paris Peace Conference?*   *p. 491*
Clemenceau, Lloyd George, Orlando, Wilson

Write Your Own Test: True-False

Write a *false* statement about the relationship between each set of words.

21. *The United States joined the Central Powers on April 6, 1917.*   *p. 481*
United States, Central Powers

22. *Germany was the most powerful member of the Triple Entente.*   *p. 476*
Germany, Triple Entente

23. *Britain respected America's neutral rights at sea throughout World War I.*   *p. 480*
Britain, America's neutral rights

24. *The War Industries Board attempted to regulate wages and safety standards in industry.*   *p. 483*
War Industries Board, wages

25. *Wilson's Fourteen Points supported reparations and opposed a League of Nations.*   *p. 490*
Fourteen Points, League of Nations

26. *The United States Senate approved the Treaty of Versailles on January 18, 1919.*   *p. 492*
Senate, Treaty of Versailles

American Republic

Decade of Change: From Progressivism to Normalcy ☆ *Classroom discussion*

After World War I interrupted the Progressive Era (1901-1916), Americans wanted a "return to normalcy." But the horrors of the war had broken their faith in progressivism. Complete this chart to see some of the changes that took place in the postwar United States.

		Progressivism	Normalcy
Foreign Relations	**Decade(s)**	*1900s and 1910s (Chapters 21-22)*	*1920s*
	Names of Presidents	*Theodore Roosevelt; William Howard Taft; Woodrow Wilson pp. 463, 466-67*	*Warren G. Harding; Calvin Coolidge; Herbert Hoover pp. 507-10*
	Concern with Foreign Affairs	*Roosevelt Corollary; "big stick" policy; "dollar diplomacy"; "moral diplomacy"; Open Door Policy pp. 444-46*	*isolationism; arms reduction; rejection of the League of Nations p. 495*
	Buildup of Navy	*arms race (Great White Fleet) p. 447*	*Treaty of Washington (shipbuilding limits) p. 495*
	Peace Treaties	*Treaty of Portsmouth (to maintain a balance of power in Asia)*	*rejection of the Treaty of Versailles; Kellogg-Briand Peace Pact (to outlaw war) p. 495*
Labor	**Farm Economy**	*economic boom p. 495*	*no markets for surpluses; low prices pp. 495-96, 509*
	Immigration	*mass immigration from southern and eastern Europe p. 496*	*quotas limiting immigrants from southern and eastern Europe p. 496*
	Labor Unions and Strikes	*"square deal" for labor (federal settlement of the United Mine Workers' strike) p. 464*	*less interest in labor unions; government raids on radical organizations pp. 497, 501*
Lifestyle	**Humanitarian Goals**	*reform of society; philanthropy; temperance; muckrakers pp. 454, 457, 461*	*none (desire for personal prosperity and pleasure) p. 494*
	Rural Life	*isolation; lack of mobility; few gadgets pp. 498-500*	*mobility; electricity; gadgets; radio pp. 498-500*
	Attitudes Toward Business	*government regulation of trade and trust busting pp. 464-65*	*government and public support of business; no interference p. 501*
Morality	**Moral Standards**	*progressive idealism; reform of corruption; social gospel; liberalism; agnosticism pp. 456-59*	*materialism; "live-for-today" attitude; crime; rejection of Christianity; moral relativity pp. 502, 505*
	Attitudes Toward Prohibition	*temperance societies; passage of Eighteenth Amendment pp. 457, 469*	*speakeasies; bootlegging; repeal of prohibition pp. 504-5*
	Presidential Leadership	*aggressive support of progressive reform, trust busting, and conservation pp. 464-65*	*political inaction; support of business; scandal pp. 501, 507-8*

American Republic

Chapter 24   Activity B

Impact of Technology  ☆ *Classroom discussion*

For each invention write the date of its first success in America, its creator(s), changes it caused in daily life, famous people associated with its industry, and changes it caused in industry. Bonus: Write changes each invention caused in warfare.

	Automobile	Airplane	Radio	Motion Picture
Date	1893 *pp. 498-99*	1903 *p. 499*	1895 *p. 500*	1889 *p. 502*
Creator(s)	*Duryea brothers*	*Wright brothers*	*Guglielmo Marconi*	*Thomas Edison*
Changes in Daily Life	*easy access to towns for shopping and social activities; rise of suburbs; traffic jams; automobile accidents; increased mobility*	*air circus entertainment; rapid transportation of mail and passengers*	*mass communication of news, music, and entertainment; fading of regional differences*	*new popular entertainment; rise of national idols; imitation of movie stars*
Famous People	*Henry Ford*	*Charles Lindbergh*	*Jack Benny; Rudy Vallee; Will Rogers*	*Clara Bow; Greta Garbo; Mary Pickford; Rudolf Valentino; Douglas Fairbanks; Buster Keaton; Charlie Chaplin*
Changes in Industry	*service stations; drive-in restaurants; motels; paved roads; businesses built near roads*	*airmail; aviation industry*	*growth of electric industry; radio manufacturing; modern advertising; radio stations*	*film industry*
Changes in Warfare	*rapid movement of troops and supplies*	*reconnaissance; bombing; end of trench warfare; new threat to ships*	*rapid communication*	*propaganda tool*

Skill: Analysis

American Republic

Chapter 24   Activity C

Sports Trivia (Exploring the *World Almanac*)

Keeping up with sports trivia became increasingly popular in the 1920s. With the help of your textbook and the *World Almanac,* see how many bits of trivia you can find.

1. Where were the Olympic Games played in 1924? _Paris_____

2. When were the first official Winter Olympic Games held? _1924_____

3. What American hockey team won the Stanley Cup in 1928? _N.Y. Rangers_____

4. In what year did Man o' War win the Preakness and Belmont Stakes? _1920_____

5. Who won the famous Rose Bowl football match of 1925? _Notre Dame_____

6. Which teams played in three Rose Bowls apiece in the 1920s? _Stanford; California_

7. How many U.S. Open Championships did Helen Wills (Moody) win in a row? _three_

8. What male tennis star won seven U.S. Open Championships in the 1920s? _Bill Tilden_

9. How many years in a row did the U.S. win the Davis Cup in the 1920s? _seven____

10. How many years was Jack Dempsey the heavyweight boxing champion? _eight_____

11. What speed did DePaolo's Duesenberg average in the 1925 Indianapolis 500? _101 MPH_

12. Who was the U.S. chess champion from 1909 to 1936? _Frank Marshall_____

13. How many times did Bobby Jones win the U.S. Open in golf? _four_____

14. What baseball team won four major league pennants in a row in the 1920s? _New York_

15. How many years was Babe Ruth the top American League home run hitter? _twelve_

16. Who was the National League batting champion six years straight? _Rogers Hornsby_

Presidents of the '20s

Match the presidents and the related terms. (Some terms apply to more than one president.)

A. Harding
B. Coolidge
C. Hoover

ABC 1. Republican   *pp. 507-10*

_A_ 2. "return to normalcy"   *p. 495*

_A_ 3. Treaty of Washington   *p. 495*

_B_ 4. Kellogg-Briand Peace Pact   *p. 495*

_A_ 5. "Ohio Gang"   *p. 508*

_A_ 6. Albert B. Fall   *p. 508*

ABC 7. pro-business   *p. 507*

_A_ 8. Teapot Dome Scandal   *pp. 508-9*

_A_ 9. heart attack   *p. 509*

_C_ 10. Great Depression   *p. 510*

American Republic

Lessons from History

Here are some of the most quoted names and events from the 1920s. Match each name or event with the lesson that it *best* illustrates.

A. Sacco and Vanzetti
B. Freud and Darwin
C. Al Capone
D. Scopes trial
E. Ku Klux Klan
F. flappers
G. movie idols
H. speculation

I. automobile accidents
J. "return to normalcy"
K. *The Man Nobody Knows*
L. Treaty of Washington
M. Teapot Dome Scandal
N. Red Scare
O. Great Depression

__F__ 1. The horrors of war often cause a breakdown in moral values. *p. 502*

__E__ 2. When the economy is bad, prejudice and racism increase. *p. 496*

__A__ 3. Prejudice against unpopular beliefs can cause great injustice, even in a democracy. *p. 497*

__H__ 4. During great prosperity, nations become materialistic and forget humanitarian goals. *pp. 497, 501*

__I__ 5. New technology brings unexpected problems as well as benefits. *pp. 498-99*

__G__ 6. Worldly rebels are the source of many fads and fashions. *p. 502*

__C__ 7. One sign of moral decay is an excessive interest in gangsters and sensationalism. *p. 505*

__K__ 8. The bias of each generation prevents people from interpreting Scripture properly. *p. 501*

__J__ 9. After the trauma of war, society often idealizes the past. *p. 495*

__L__ 10. Agreements to reduce arms are ineffective because nations make many exceptions. *p. 495*

__N__ 11. When a nation has a dangerous enemy, the people often overreact to the threat. *p. 497*

__D__ 12. God says that Christians will be scorned if they take a stand for their faith. *pp. 505-7*

__B__ 13. People accept many foolish ideas in the name of "science" because the ideas justify sin. *p. 505*

__M__ 14. When good men do nothing, evil flourishes. *pp. 508-9*

__O__ 15. The pleasures of this world last only a season. *p. 510*

Thought Questions: What names or events from this chapter illustrate these lessons?

16. Men cannot establish lasting peace on their own. _Kellogg-Briand Peace Pact_
     (and World War II) *p. 495*

17. Laws cannot change people's moral character. _prohibition (speakeasies, bootlegging)_
     _pp. 504-5_

18. Liberalism may force Christians to leave their jobs or churches. _J. Gresham Machen_ *p. 506*

19. A president is often blamed for problems caused by his predecessor. _Herbert Hoover_ *p. 510*

American Republic

News Flash, 1920s Style

The radio put the average American in touch with events as they happened. Write a few sentences summarizing what the radio announcer might have said for each event below. Be sure to include the five *W*s.

The "Bull" Makes a Million [July 2, 1921] __We interrupt this program with a news flash from__ __the ringside at Jersey City, N.J. The "bull" Jack Dempsey has laid another man low with his__ __iron fists. In a bout lasting only four rounds, Dempsey has cashed in the world's first__ __"million-dollar gate" and won a place in the history books. What a mauler!   p. 503__

Treaty Saves Shipbuilding Cost [December 13, 1921] __This report just came in from__ __Washington. To avoid future temptation for war, the world's naval powers have signed a__ __historic treaty agreeing to trim down their navies. For every five British or American ships__ __built, Japan has agreed to build three and France and Italy, one and three-quarters.   p. 495__

President Dies [August 2, 1923] __We interrupt this program to report a tragedy. President__ __Harding is dead! According to initial reports, he got food poisoning while vacationing in__ __Alaska. What a tragic day for the nation! We will keep you informed as new reports come in.__ __p. 509__

Scandal Confirmed in the Interior Department [January 25, 1924] __Hold on to your seats__ __for this one! Testimony before the Senate has just confirmed that former Interior Secretary__ __Albert B. Fall received "loans" for leasing navy oil reserves at Teapot Dome, Wyoming.__ __Reporters are calling it the scandal of the century.   pp. 508-9__

Teacher Convicted in Monkey Trial [July 21, 1925] __We interrupt this program with an__ __update on the Monkey Trial in Dayton, Tennessee. The judge has just convicted John Scopes__ __of teaching evolution and fined him $100. Bryan is satisfied but exhausted. Darrow is furious.__ __pp. 506-7__

Spelunker Breathes His Last [February 16, 1925] __We interrupt this program with a news__ __flash from Kentucky. The intrepid spelunker Floyd Collins, trapped for eighteen days in Sand__ __Cave, has breathed his last. He gave no reply when reporters visited him today. What a grave!__ __p. 503__

Wonder Dog Saves Lives [December 8, 1925] ___We interrupt this program with a news flash___ ___from Nome, Alaska. Balto successfully led his team of dogs 655 miles through a blinding___ ___blizzard to carry antitoxin to Eskimos suffering from a fatal case of diphtheria. Temperatures___ ___were so low that the thermometers broke!   p. 503___

Woman Swims the Channel [August 6, 1926] ___We interrupt this program with a news flash___ ___from England. The swimming wonder Gertrude Ederle has successfully completed her___ ___twenty-two-mile swim across the English Channel, the first woman in history to set this___ ___record. Can you believe it?   p. 503___

Lucky Lindy Lands [May 21, 1927] ___We interrupt this program with a news flash from Paris.___ ___"The Lone Eagle" Lindbergh has landed his Spirit of St. Louis after a grueling thirty-three___ ___and one-half hour transatlantic flight from New York to Paris. The city has gone wild! It's___ ___the greatest achievement in aviation history!   p. 499___

Two Communists Executed [August 23, 1927] ___We interrupt this program with a special report___ ___from Massachusetts. The infamous Italian anarchists, Sacco and Vanzetti, have been___ ___electrocuted for the murder of two shoe company employees during a robbery. Angry___ ___protests are being held around the world.   p. 497___

War Outlawed [August 27, 1928] ___Here's some hot news from Paris. Secretary of State___ ___Kellogg has joined French minister Briand and other world leaders in a pact outlawing war.___ ___The Peace Pact was hailed as the greatest move towards world peace in two thousand years.___ ___p. 495___

Relief Administrator Becomes President [November 6, 1928] ___Herbert Hoover, the talented___ ___relief administrator from the Great War, now has a chance to try his hand at the presidency.___ ___He easily defeated Democrat Al Smith, an anti-Prohibition Roman Catholic. The nation is___ ___celebrating the prospects of four more years of unprecedented prosperity.   pp. 509-10___

American Republic

Chapter 25   Activity A

Hoover vs. FDR  *Classroom discussion*

Rarely have two successive presidents been more different. Hoover was a self-made westerner; Roosevelt, a rich-born easterner. Complete the chart to see their major differences. (Refer to Chapter 25 and pages 509-10 in the text.)

	Herbert Hoover	**Franklin Delano Roosevelt**
Terms	*one p. 509*	*four p. 523*
Party	*Republican p. 509*	*Democrat p. 523*
Occupation	*engineer p. 509*	*lawyer p. 523*
Home	*West Branch, Iowa p. 509*	*Hyde Park, New York p. 523*
Religion	*Quaker p. 509*	*Episcopalian p. 523*
Domestic Conditions	*Prosperity ended with the crash and despair. A run on banks forced many to close. One worker in four was unemployed. Many people suffered in "Hoovervilles." Farmers suffered in the Dust Bowl. pp. 516-19*	*People felt confident about the future. Fewer banks closed. The nation did not enjoy a real recovery until World War II. Small improvements ended in recession. pp. 522-24, 526, 529-30*
Views of Federal Assistance	*Communities are responsible to ease hardship. Government agencies breed red tape. Federal funds should be carefully regulated. He opposed regulation of business. He feared socialism and supported freedom. He sought a balanced budget. He praised traditional "rugged individualism." pp. 521, 523*	*He proposed vigorous government action. He offered a long line of legislation. He handed out doles. He regulated banks, agriculture, and business. He experimented with radical socialism. He created an enormous debt. He offered an untried "New Deal." pp. 522-27, 530*
Major Programs	*Hoover Dam; road building; Reconstruction Finance Corporation; Federal District Home Loans Banks pp. 521-22*	*Emergency Banking Act; Federal Emergency Relief Administration; Agriculture Adjustment Act; National Recovery Administration; Civilian Conservation Corps; Tennessee Valley Authority; Works Progress Administration; Social Security pp. 523-27*
Public Reaction	*Americans blamed Hoover for the depression and criticized his reluctance to take dramatic action. pp. 521-22*	*Most Americans trusted FDR and were pleased with his firm action. Liberals wanted more action; conservatives wanted less. pp. 526-28, 530*
Success of Programs	*Americans continued to suffer and remained discontent, but Hoover protected traditional American values. pp. 521-22*	*Americans regained hope even though suffering continued, but FDR only covered problems and set dangerous precedents. p. 530*

Reinforcement: Sections 1-3

Skill: Charts   **147**

American Republic

Evaluating the New Deal   ☆ *Classroom discussion*

Roosevelt had two aims: to relieve America's immediate hardships and to reform the long-term causes of these hardships. For each problem summarize FDR's solutions, the effectiveness of his solutions, and problems with these solutions. Each summary should include the terms given in parentheses.

1. Lack of Confidence in America's Future

   Solutions (New Deal, Brain Trust, fireside chats):

   FDR promised the voters "vigorous action" and a New Deal. He borrowed ideas from a Brain Trust of college professors. In his radio fireside chats and his press conferences, he radiated warmth and rallied support for his ideas.   pp. 522-23

   Effectiveness ("rubber stamp," reelection): *Congress, seeing Roosevelt's popular support, became a "rubber stamp" for New Deal legislation. Roosevelt easily won reelection. pp. 524, 528-30*

   Problems (Democratic Party, executive branch): *Roosevelt used his popularity to change the Democratic Party's image to that of a friend of the underprivileged and to increase the power of government, particularly the power of the executive branch.   pp. 528-29*

2. Bank Collapse

   Solutions (Emergency Banking Act, Home Owners' Loan Corporation, gold standard):

   The Emergency Banking Act created a bank holiday until banks could restabilize. The Home Owners' Loan Corporation bought mortgages from holders and rewrote them on easier terms. America went off the gold standard.   pp. 524, 530

   Effectiveness (payment schedules): *Depositors' confidence in the banks improved. The payment schedules for many nonfarm mortgages were reduced.   p. 524*

   Problems (federal power): *The end of the gold standard did little to aid the economy, but the federal power to control currency and banking increased dramatically.   pp. 530-31*

3. Unemployment

Solutions (FERA, WPA, CCC, Social Security): _FERA gave direct relief. Its successor,_ _the WPA, provided work relief in construction. The CCC gave young people jobs in_ _conservation. Social Security insured Americans against various misfortunes._ _pp. 524, 526-27_

Effectiveness (conservation): _The CCC encouraged hard work and conservation._ _p. 526_

Problems (dole, faith): _Most of FERA's money went out as a dole. The many programs_ _encouraged people to place their faith in government rather than God._ _pp. 524, 531_

4. Low Farm Prices

Solutions (AAA): _The Farm Credit Administration refinanced mortgages for_ _desperate farmers. The AAA paid farmers to destroy their crops and to avoid planting_ _new crops._ _p. 524_

Effectiveness (prices, income): _Food prices went up and farm income increased_ _fifty percent over two years._ _p. 524_

Problems (subsidies, sharecropper): _Farmers became dependent on subsidies._ _Landowners, not needy sharecroppers, received money. Government regulation was_ _expensive and hampered the free market._ _pp. 524-25_

5. Business Slump

Solutions (NRA, TVA, Wagner Act, minimum wage): _The NRA wrote business codes and_ _assigned each business a share of the market. TVA provided for public power projects on_ _the Tennessee River. The Wagner Act supported labor. Later the Fair Labor Standards Act_ _set the first minimum wage at twenty-five cents._ _pp. 525-27_

Effectiveness (rural electricity, labor unions): _Rural electricity increased. The power of_ _labor unions also increased._ _pp. 526-27_

Problems (socialism, court packing, recession): _Roosevelt's programs encouraged socialism,_ _not free enterprise. Conservative opposition from the Supreme Court led to a court-packing_ _plan. After years of government involvement, the country had a recession in 1937._ _pp. 528-30_

American Republic

Graphing Negative Numbers: Between the Wars (1920-1939)

Government Overspending (in billions): Choose the best type of graph (line or bar) to make to illustrate these data from the Census Bureau. (Hint: Overspending is indicated by a *negative* difference.)

Year	1920	'21	'22	'23	'24	'25	'26	'27	'28	'29	'30	'31	'32	'33	'34	'35	'36	'37	'38	'39	'40
Income	6.6	5.6	4.0	3.9	3.9	3.6	3.8	4.0	3.9	3.8	4.0	3.2	2.0	2.1	3.1	3.8	4.2	5.6	7.0	6.6	6.9
Spending	6.4	5.1	3.3	3.1	2.9	2.9	2.9	2.9	3.0	2.9	3.1	4.1	4.8	4.7	6.5	6.3	7.6	8.4	7.2	9.4	9.6
Difference	.2	.5	.7	.8	1.0	.7	.9	1.1	.9	.9	.9	-.9	-2.8	-2.6	-3.4	-2.5	-3.4	-2.8	-.2	-2.8	-2.7

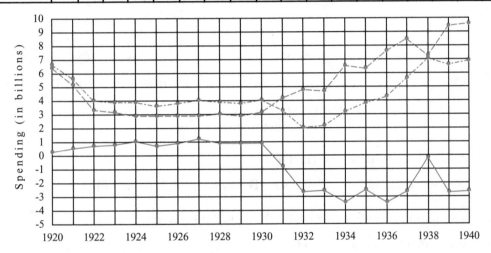

Boom and Crash: GNP means "gross national product." GNP growth shows the ups and downs of American business. Use blue bars to plot GNP increases and red bars to plot GNP declines.

Year	1920	'21	'22	'23	'24	'25	'26	'27	'28	'29	'30	'31	'32	'33	'34	'35	'36	'37	'38	'39	'40
GNP Growth	-8.6	15.8	12.1	-.2	8.4	5.9	0	.6	6.7	-9.8	-7.6	-14.7	-1.8	9.1	9.9	13.9	5.3	-5.0	8.6	8.5	16.1

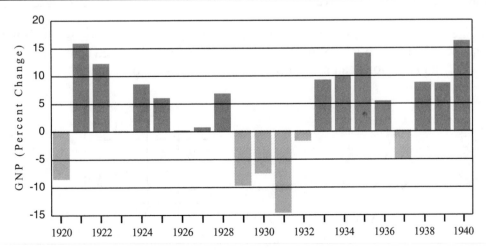

American Republic

Modified True/False

If the statement is true, write *true* in the blank. If it is false, change the underlined words to make the statement true.

_____*true*___*p. 514*_____ 1. The Great Depression began after the stock market crashed on "Black Thursday" (October 24, <u>1929</u>).

_____*Florida*___*p. 515*_____ 2. The biggest land speculation in the '20s was in <u>California</u>.

_____*down*___*p. 516*_____ 3. Buying on the margin was risky because the broker could "call" in the buyer's margin if stock prices went too far <u>up</u>.

_____*Germany*___*p. 516*_____ 4. The Allies repaid their war debts with money that the U.S. loaned to <u>France</u>.

_____*government*___*p. 531*_____ 5. The hardships of the Great Depression caused many Americans to re-examine their values and turn to <u>Jesus Christ</u> for help.

_____*true*___*p. 519*_____ 6. Overgrazing and drought turned the plains into a <u>Dust Bowl</u>.

_____*veterans*___*p. 520*_____ 7. The Bonus Army was composed of <u>retired workers</u> who wanted to receive their life insurance early.

The New Deal's "Alphabet Soup"

In each blank write the initials of the New Deal program that each phrase describes.

1. gave the Blue Eagle seal to businesses that complied with government codes _*NRA*___*p. 525*_

2. provided part-time jobs for students _*NYA*___*p. 527*_

3. refinanced mortgages for farmers who would have lost their lands _*FCA*___*p. 524*_

4. paid farmers to destroy their crops and leave their fields unplanted _*AAA*___*p. 524*_

5. hired unemployed young men to help conserve natural resources _*CCC*___*p. 526*_

6. dispersed $500 million, mostly as doles _*FERA*___*p. 524*_

7. provided electricity to many rural areas _*TVA*___*p. 526*_

Now create your own word search for these seven New Deal programs. Arrange the letters in the "alphabet soup" so that the abbreviations appear somewhere in the word search. (The abbreviations can run horizontally, vertically, or diagonally.)

```
A   F   T   Y
A   C   R
N   E   A
C   A   C
```

	F	C	T
N	E	C	V
Y	R	C	A
A	A	A	

Skill: Comprehension

American Republic

Chapter 26   Activity A

Steps to War    ☆ *Classroom discussion*

Although America's turnaround from total isolationism to all-out war seemed sudden, it was provoked by a long series of events. To complete the chart, choose the *best* answers from the list on the back. Refer to Chapters 23-25 for some of the earlier events.

Cause	Foreign Action	American Reaction
Allies' desire to humiliate Germany pp. 491-92, 495	Treaty of Versailles (1919)	*disillusionment with foreign wars*
Allies' desire to limit the arms race p. 495	Treaty of Washington (1921)	*hope that naval competition would cease*
Allies' fear of future war p. 495	Kellogg-Briand Peace Pact (1928)	*hope that nations would avoid war to settle disputes*
Japan's disappointment with its lack of recognition after World War I p. 535	Japan's conquest of Manchuria (1931)	*disappointment after appealing to the League of Nations*
worldwide depression	Allies' failure to pay war debts (early 1930s)	*bitterness at the Allies' ingratitude*
Italy's disappointment with its spoils after World War I p. 534	Italy's conquest of Ethiopia (1935)	*horror at fascist aggression, but no action*
the Führer's repudiation of the Versailles Treaty p. 534	Germany's capture of the Rhineland (1936)	*no protests at the violation of the Versailles Treaty*
Hitler's request for the Sudetenland p. 536	Britain's appeasement (1938)	*realization of the Nazi threat to peace*
Germany's blitzkrieg into Poland p. 537	Allied declaration of war (1939)	*"cash-and-carry" policy p. 539*
Germany's blitzkrieg through Belgium pp. 537-38	fall of France (1940)	*"lend-lease" policy p. 540*
Japan's alliance with the Axis powers pp. 540-41	Japan's entry into Southeast Asia (1941)	*ban on most trade with Japan*
Hitler's stalemate with Britain p. 538	Germany's invasion of Russia (1941)	*secret agreement with Churchill to defeat "Hitler first"*
Roosevelt's decision to send convoys with "lend-lease" supplies p. 540	Germany's sinking of U.S. convoys (1941)	*decision to shoot submarines on sight*
Japan's desire to strengthen its position in Asia p. 541	Japan's attack on Pearl Harbor (1941)	*declaration of war against the Axis powers*

153

Causes

Germany's blitzkrieg into Poland
Germany's blitzkrieg through Belgium
Allies' desire to limit the arms race
Allies' fear of future war
Allies' desire to humiliate Germany
Hitler's stalemate with Britain
Hitler's request for the Sudetenland
the Führer's repudiation of the Versailles Treaty
Japan's alliance with the Axis powers
Japan's desire to strengthen its position in Asia
Japan's disappointment with its lack of recognition after World War I
Italy's disappointment with its spoils after World War I
Roosevelt's decision to send convoys with "lend-lease" supplies

American Reactions

"lend-lease" policy
"cash-and-carry" policy
ban on most trade with Japan
disillusionment with foreign wars
declaration of war against the Axis powers
hope that naval competition would cease
horror at fascist aggression, but no action
hope that nations would avoid war to settle disputes
no protests at the violation of the Versailles Treaty
disappointment after appealing to the League of Nations

Review Questions

Answer these questions based on the textbook and the chart on the previous page.

1   What Nazi leader repudiated (violated) the Versailles Treaty? _Adolf Hitler   p. 534_

2. What dictator began the "Second Roman Empire" by conquering Ethiopia? _Benito Mussolini p. 534_

3. What were the first two Axis powers? _Germany and Italy   p. 535_

4. How many years passed before Japan violated the Kellogg-Briand Peace Pact? _three (chart)_

5. Who introduced the Good Neighbor Policy? _Herbert Hoover   p. 535_

6. What dictator signed a pact with Hitler after Britain's appeasement? _Joseph Stalin   p. 537_

7. How many years passed between Britain's appeasement and declaration of war? _one (chart)_

8. What was the first country to fall under Germany's blitzkrieg? _Poland   p. 537_

9. What shocking event encouraged America to pass the Lend-Lease Act? _fall of France (chart)_

10. How many years did Britain fight before America joined World War II? _two (chart)_

11. What country stopped Hitler with a "scorched earth" policy? _Soviet Union   p. 539_

12. What Japanese action caused the U.S. to declare war on Germany? _attack on Pearl Harbor   p. 541_

American Republic

Alternative Outlining

Discuss the differences between these outlines and the advantages of each. Also discuss other ways to outline.

You can usually organize information in more than one way. First, copy the simple outline given in the chapter. Then move the elements of the outline to fit the alternative outline.

A. Trouble Brewing
   1. *Leaders of War   p. 534*
   2. *Roosevelt and Foreign Policy   p. 535*

B. World War II Begins
   1. *German Expansion   p. 536*
   2. *War Envelops Europe   p. 537*
   3. *Britain Stands Alone   p. 538*
   4. *Hitler Turns Against the Soviet Union   p. 538*
   5. *American Sympathies and Fears   p. 539*

C. America Enters the War
   1. *Manpower for War   p. 541*
   2. *Materials for War   p. 542*
   3. *Mapping the War   p. 543*

D. American Efforts in Europe
   1. *Attacking North Africa   p. 544*
   2. *The Allies Attack Italy   p. 544*
   3. *Invasion at Normandy   p. 545*
   4. *German Defeat   p. 546*

E. The War in the Pacific
   1. *The Japanese Advance   p. 547*
   2. *The Rising Sun Begins to Set   p. 548*
   3. *MacArthur Moves Northward   p. 549*
   4. *Nimitz Moves West   p. 550*

F. The End of the War
   1. *The Beginning of the Atomic Era   p. 551*
   2. *Peace   p. 552*

A. World War Returns
   1. *Leaders of War*
   2. *German Expansion*
   3. *War Envelops Europe*
   4. *Britain Stands Alone*
   5. *Hitler Turns Against the Soviet Union*

B. America Prepares for War
   1. *Roosevelt and Foreign Policy*
   2. *American Sympathies and Fears*
   3. *Manpower for War*
   4. *Materials for War*
   5. *Mapping the War*

C. American Campaigns in Europe
   1. *Attacking North Africa*
   2. *The Allies Attack Italy*
   3. *Invasion at Normandy*

D. American Campaigns in the Pacific
   1. *The Japanese Advance*
   2. *The Rising Sun Begins to Set*
   3. *MacArthur Moves Northward*
   4. *Nimitz Moves West*

E. Defeat of the Axis
   1. *German Defeat*
   2. *The Beginning of the Atomic Era*
   3. *Peace*

American Republic

War in Two Theaters

Americans' experiences in the Pacific differed greatly from their experiences in Europe. Complete the chart showing the major differences between these two theaters of war.

		European Theater	Pacific Theater
Resources	**Geographic Features**	North African desert, Italian mountains, and French beaches and plains pp. 544-46	tropical islands, large ocean pp. 547-49
	Allied Nations	U.S., Great Britain, and Soviet Union (also France) p. 538	U.S. (also China, Great Britain, Australia, Philippines, Soviet Union) p. 547
	Allied Commanders	Dwight D. Eisenhower (also Clark, Bradley, Patton, and Montgomery) pp. 544-45	Douglas MacArthur and Chester Nimitz pp. 547, 549
	Axis Nations	Germany and Italy p. 541	Japan p. 541
	Axis Commanders	Erwin Rommel p. 544	Yamamoto Isoroku and Masaharu Homma
Allied Strategy	**Campaign Plans**	"Hitler first"; Operation Torch (retake Africa); Operation Husky (invade Sicily/Italy); Operation Overlord (invade Normandy) pp. 543-45	resist Japanese advances first; then push north to Philippines and "island-hop" west to Japan pp. 547-49
	Role of Planes	bomb industrial and military sites by day; protect ground troops pp. 545-46	attack opposing airplanes and fleets; bomb islands; drop atomic bombs pp. 548-49, 552
	Role of Ships	move invading troops and supplies pp. 544-46	carry planes; fight enemy fleets; bomb islands; move and support invading troops pp. 548-49
	Role of Tanks	maneuver swiftly through Africa and France pp. 544-46	none
	Role of Troops	land on beaches and advance quickly over open terrain pp. 544-46	fight slow, bloody battles for islands pp. 549-51
Battles	**First Battle**	Operation Torch (North Africa) p. 544	Pearl Harbor p. 547
	Lost Battles	none	Pearl Harbor and the Philippines (Bataan and Corregidor) pp. 547-48
	Turning Point	D-Day invasion p. 546	battles of the Coral Sea and Midway p. 549
	Last Big Battle	battle of the Bulge p. 546	Okinawa p. 551
	Date of Victory	May 8, 1945 (V-E Day) p. 547	September 2, 1945 pp. 552-53

American Republic

Map Study: The Rubber Band Snaps in Europe

When the tiny RAF stopped the advancing Nazi giant, Churchill believed he had struck a deadly blow. Yet Britain was still alone. Why was Churchill so confident?

The Third Reich was like a rubber band. The more it stretched, the more difficult its position became. As long as Britain stayed in the war, the conquered peoples resisted their German conquerors. Each time Hitler took a country, he had to send more troops and supplies to guard it. The wider his borders became, the greater the demand on his limited supply of soldiers and war equipment. The discouraged soldiers also marched farther and farther from their homes and supplies in Berlin.

With the help of American "lend-lease," the Allies were able to hold the line. Later, as American GIs began to arrive, the pressure on the overstretched Nazi empire became irresistible. You will see how the Nazi "rubber band" snapped after you complete this map study. Refer to the maps in the textbook on pages 539 and 545.

1. Label the Mediterranean Sea.

2. Using a black pencil, label these countries that were controlled by the Axis at its height: France (Fr.), Belgium (Bel.), The Netherlands (Neth.), Germany (Ger.), Austria (Aus.), Italy (It.), Czechoslovakia (Czech.), Poland (Pol.), Denmark (Den.), Norway (Nor.), Finland (Fin.), Yugoslavia (Yug.), Albania (Alb.), Greece (Gr.), Hungary (Hun.), Rumania (Rum.), Bulgaria (Bulg.), Tunisia (Tun.).

3. Using a green pencil, label these countries that were Allies at the end of 1941: Britain (Br.) and the Soviet Union (USSR).

4. Using a red pencil, label these battle sites: London, Paris, Berlin, Sicily, Rome, Normandy, Bastogne.

5. Compare the two maps in the textbook. Then shade the territory that changed sides between the two periods depicted on the maps.

6. Draw these figures at the appropriate places:

 battle of the Bulge
p. 546

 battle of Britain
p. 538

Rommel's Korps
p. 544

D-Day invasion
pp. 545-46

 the 1939 blitzkrieg
p. 537

every 1940 blitzkrieg
p. 537

the major 1941 blitzkrieg
pp. 538-39

escape from Dunkirk
pp. 537-38

 Operation Husky
p. 544

Operation Torch
p. 544

conquests by appeasement
p. 536

Map Questions (optional)

Using the map scales in the text on pages 539 and 545, give the approximate distances below.

Students should make quick approximations. This will help them see the extensive borders that were impossible to keep.

from Berlin to London __*600 mi.*__

from Berlin to Moscow __*1000 mi.*__

from Berlin to Tunisia __*1100 mi.*__

from Berlin to Normandy __*650 mi.*__

Germany's original border (1935) __*2500± mi.*__

French coastline (1941) __*1500± mi.*__

Axis border with USSR (1941) __*1000± mi.*__

total Axis border in Europe (1941) __*6500± mi.*__

American Republic

Map Study: The Balloon Pops in the Pacific

The Japanese knew they could never conquer the "sleeping giant" America. So their war plan had two phases: (1) with a burst of energy, they would destroy America's fleet at Pearl Harbor and capture a wide circle of islands around Japan; then (2) they would defend these islands with troops, planes, and ships until America lost its will to fight.

But they made two serious mistakes. First, their initial successes encouraged them to stretch beyond their safe circle of islands (at Midway and the Coral Sea) and waste their limited strength. Second, they misjudged America's technology and will to fight.

America realized that Japan could not send its warships everywhere at once, nor did it have enough "gas" (supplies) to keep its leaky "balloon" inflated for long. So by air, land, and sea America attacked from two directions at once.

When the U.S. captured the Marianas, even the Japanese knew that defeat was coming. But as the "balloon" shrank, its skin became tougher. America's plan for final victory had three parts: (1) unrestricted submarine warfare to sink merchant ships and starve Japan, (2) fire bombing to destroy Japan's cities and will to fight, and (3) landing troops on Japan itself. But a new weapon—the atomic bomb—ended the war.

Refer to the map on page 548 of your textbook.

1. Using a black pencil, label the regions that Japan controlled after World War I: Japan (including Tokyo), Korea, Okinawa, Iwo Jima, Mariana Islands, Marshall Islands.

2. Using a brown pencil, label the regions that Japan attacked before December 7, 1941: Manchuria (1931), China (1937), French Indochina (1940).

3. Using a red pencil, label the regions that Japan attacked during the winter of 1941-42: Pearl Harbor, Guam, Wake Island, Philippines, Singapore, Thailand, Netherlands East Indies, New Guinea, Burma, Solomon Islands (including Guadalcanal).

4. Using a black pencil, draw a "balloon" around Japan's empire at its height.

5. Using a green pencil, label the two regions Japan hoped to capture in the spring of 1942: Coral Sea, Midway Island.

6. Using a blue pencil, draw lines showing each successive indentation that the U.S. made in Japan's balloon. Label with a Roman numeral each region that the U.S. captured.

   • Nimitz in the Central Pacific: (I) Tarawa (fall '43), (II) Marshall Islands (winter '43), (III) Mariana Islands and Guam (summer '44), (IV) Iwo Jima (winter '44)

   • MacArthur in the Southwest Pacific: (I) Guadalcanal (fall '42) and the Solomon Islands (fall '43), (II) New Guinea (winter '43), (III) Philippines (fall/winter '44), (IV) Okinawa (spring '45)

7. Draw these figures at the appropriate places:

 first atomic bomb *p. 552*

 day of "infamy" *p. 533*

 sea battle by planes *p. 549*

 best base for bombing Japan
p. 551

 Doolittle raid *p. 548*

 Bataan "death march" *p. 547*

 costliest marine battle *p. 550*

 cracked Japanese code *p. 549*

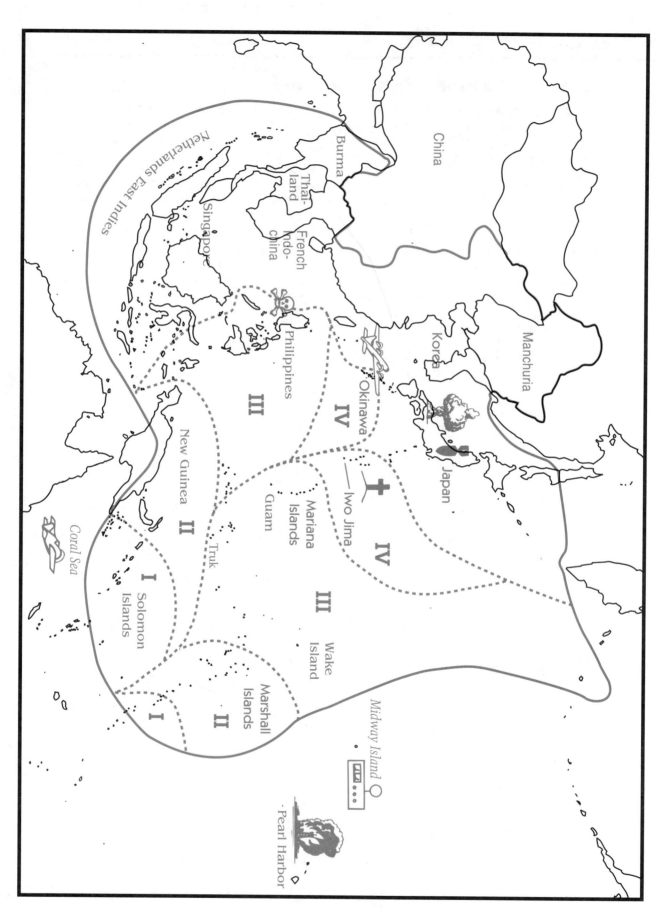

China

Manchuria

Korea

Japan

Burma

Thai-
land

French
Indo-
china

Netherlands East Indies

Singapore

Philippines

Okinawa

Iwo Jima

Mariana
Islands

Guam

Wake
Island

Marshall
Islands

New Guinea

Truk

Solomon
Islands

Coral Sea

Midway Island

Pearl Harbor

III

IV

IV

III

II

II

I

I

American Republic

Breaking the Code

The United States employed many different professionals in its effort to win World War II, including riveters, entertainers, nuclear scientists, spies, and cryptographers. A cryptographer is a code-breaker. Breaking secret codes has had a decisive impact on war, especially the Zimmermann telegram in World War I and the Japanese attack on Midway in World War II.

One of the best-kept secrets in military history was the Manhattan Project. Even Harry S. Truman did not know about it until after he became president. Here is a top-secret message that President Truman received on August 9, 1945, while he was at Potsdam.

ICRFCG LOH VEHF GXFEGUXI TCHF XUFLEHAOHFAR OUI
RCUPAIXUF FLOF FLX BAFFBX MCN AH OH LEHSN OH
LAH MAK MGCFLXG. FLX BAKLF AU LAH XNXH IAH-
RXGUAMBX PGCT LXGX FC LAKLLCBI OUI A RCEBI
LOWX LXOGI LAH HRGXOTH PGCT LXGX FC TN POGT.

Overall idea of message: The bomb ("Fat Boy") was as powerful as the first bomb, visible and audible from far away.

Doctor has just returned most enthusiastic and _____

confident that the little boy is as husky as _____

his big brother. The light in his eyes dis- _____

cernible from here to highhold and I could _____

have heard his screams from here to my farm. _____

The code is simple. Each code letter stands for a letter of the alphabet. The key shows you that *I* has been substituted for *D*, and *N* for *Y*.

Code	A	B	C	D	E	F	G	H	I	J	K	L	M	N	O	P	Q	R	S	T	U	V	W	X	Y	Z
Alphabet	*I*	*L*	*O*	*P*	*U*	*T*	*R*	*S*	*D*	*W*	*G*	*H*	*B*	*Y*	*A*	*F*	*X*	*C*	*K*	*M*	*N*	*J*	*V*	*E*	*Z*	*Q*

Before you can read Truman's message, you need to complete the key. So follow these instructions carefully. Below are seventeen terms written in the code and followed by a descriptive phrase. (1) Fill in each blank with the correct term *in the real alphabet*. (2) Find the real letter of the alphabet that each code letter stands for, and write it in the key above. (3) After you complete the key, decode the top-secret message above.

The students need to do only enough code-breaking activity to figure out the alphabet.

1. LAFBXG   Germany's *Führer*   HITLER   *p. 534*

2. TEHHCBAUA   Italy's *Il Duce*   MUSSOLINI   *p. 534*

3. HFOBAU   the Soviet Union's wartime dictator STALIN   *p. 537*

4. RLEGRLABB   Britain's wartime prime minister   CHURCHILL   *p. 536*

5. GCCHXWXBF   America's wartime president   ROOSEVELT   *p. 533*

6. XAHXULCJXG   America's commander in Africa   EISENHOWER   *p. 544*

7. TOROGFLEG   America's general in the Philippines MACARTHUR   *p. 547*

8. UATAFY   America's admiral in the Pacific   NIMITZ   *p. 549*

9. FGETOU   America's president at Potsdam   _TRUMAN p. 552_

10. UOYA   the fascist party in Germany   _NAZI p. 534_

11. OQAH   the alliance of fascist powers   _AXIS p. 535_

12. UXAKLMCG   FDR's "Good _____" policy   _NEIGHBOR p. 535_

13. ODDXOHXTXUF   Chamberlain's foreign policy   _APPEASEMENT p. 536_

14. POHRAHF   nationalist, dictatorial governments   _FASCIST p. 535_

15. MBAFYSGAXK   "lightning war"   _BLITZKRIEG p. 537_

16. SOTASOYXH   Japan's suicide attack planes   _KAMIKAZES p. 550_

17. CMVXRFCG   conscientious _____   _OBJECTOR p. 542_

More Terms

Identify the terms described below.

1. land occupied by Germany in violation of the Versailles Treaty   _Rhineland p. 534_

2. first country to be attacked during World War II   _Poland p. 537_

3. major Allied country that the Nazis conquered in 1940   _France p. 538_

4. act that allowed Allies to get supplies without paying money   _Lend-Lease Act p. 540_

5. naval base bombed by Japan on December 7, 1941   _Pearl Harbor p. 541_

6. first Axis power to surrender   _Italy p. 544_

7. French region attacked on D-Day   _Normandy p. 546_

8. town that Germans surrounded during the battle of the Bulge   _Bastogne p. 546_

9. meeting where FDR gave the Soviets control of Eastern Europe   _Yalta p. 546_

10. country that surrendered on V-E Day   _Germany p. 547_

11. sea where American planes stopped Japan's attack on Australia   _Coral Sea p. 549_

12. island where MacArthur began his offensive   _Guadalcanal p. 549_

13. tiny island near Tokyo where five thousand marines died   _Iwo Jima p. 550_

14. last island that Americans captured near the Japanese mainland   _Okinawa p. 551_

15. place where Truman warned Japan to surrender unconditionally   _Potsdam p. 552_

16. code name of America's atomic bomb project   _Manhattan p. 551_

17. town destroyed by the plutonium "Fat Boy"   _Nagasaki p. 552_

American Republic

Chapter 27   Activity A

The Postwar Administrations   *Classroom discussion*

Truman and Eisenhower faced many of the same problems. Complete the chart to see how postwar America took shape during their administrations. (Hint: Also refer to pp. 551-53.)

	Harry S. Truman	Dwight D. Eisenhower
Years in Office	*1945-1953 p. 552*	*1953-1961 p. 574*
Political Party	*Democratic p. 552*	*Republican p. 574*
Hometown	*Independence, Missouri p. 552*	*Abilene, Kansas p. 574*
Job in WWII	*vice president; president pp. 551-52*	*general p. 574*
Domestic Policy	*Fair Deal p. 562*	*dynamic conservatism*
Foreign Policy	*containment p. 568*	*peaceful coexistence p. 573*
Major Laws	*GI Bill; Taft-Hartley Act pp. 560, 563*	*Federal Aid Highway Act p. 561*
Major Events at Home	*beginning of baby boom; growth of urban sprawl (suburbs); beginning of sunbelt migrations; green revolution pp. 560-62*	*St. Lawrence Seaway; admission of Alaska and Hawaii pp. 574-75*
Support of Civil Rights	*President's Committee on Civil Rights; end of segregation in the military; continued Roosevelt's policy of no federal contracts with discriminatory businesses p. 563*	*Supreme Court's opposition to segregated schools (Brown v. Board of Education)*
New Alliances and International Organizations	*United Nations; North Atlantic Treaty Organization pp. 565-66, 569*	*Southeast Asia Treaty Organization p. 572*
Major Events in Europe	*Nuremberg trials; Marshall Plan; iron curtain; Berlin airlift pp. 564-65, 568-69*	*Soviet invasion of Hungary p. 573*
Major Events in Asia	*Communist takeover of China; Korean War pp. 569-70*	*North Vietnam's guerrilla war in South Vietnam p. 572*

Reinforcement: Sections 1-4

Skill: Charts

American Republic

Hot Spots During the Cold War   *Classroom discussion*

Pick four countries or regions where the United States intervened after World War II. For each region summarize communist activities, American actions, and American successes or failures. (Make sure your summary includes related terms and people.)

	Communist Activities	**United States Activities**	**U.S. Successes/Failures**
Germany	The Soviets imposed communism on East Germany and blockaded West Berlin. pp. 564, 568	The U.S. supported the Berlin airlift and allowed West Germany to form a republic. pp. 568-69	Although the U.S. failed to reunite Germany, it kept communism out of the West. p. 569
Europe	The Soviets imposed communism in the East, formed the Warsaw Pact, crushed a revolt in Hungary, and tried to spread communism in the West. pp. 565, 567-69, 573	The Marshall Plan sent billions in aid to Western Europe. The U.S. started NATO and issued the Truman Doctrine to contain communism in Europe. pp. 565, 568-69	Although Western Europe rebuilt quickly and remained free, the U.S. failed to stop the iron curtain from falling over Eastern Europe. pp. 565, 568
Korea	The Soviets imposed communism in North Korea and aided the army that invaded the South. China sent troops during the Korean War. pp. 570-71	The U.S. allowed South Korea to form a republic and led the U.N. forces that tried to stop the attack from the North. pp. 570-71	Although the U.S. failed to reunite Korea, it kept communism out of the South. pp. 571-72
Southeast Asia	When Ho Chi Minh led a revolt against the French, the U.N. gave him North Korea. He began a guerrilla war in the South with Chinese and Soviet aid. p. 572	The U.S. sent aid and advisors to South Vietnam once the U.N. granted it freedom. The U.S. joined SEATO to contain communism. pp. 572-73	The U.S. allowed North Vietnam to fall to the communists and became embroiled in South Vietnam. pp. 572-73
Cuba	Fidel Castro overthrew Batista and set up a cruel communist dictatorship, aided by the Soviets. p. 574	The State Department was aware of Castro's communist leanings, but Americans believed he would improve Cuba, so no action was taken. p. 574	The U.S. allowed a communist nation to arise ninety miles off its coast. p. 574
Japan	The Soviets were not given a part in Japan's recovery. p. 564	The U.S. helped Japan write a new constitution and sent aid to help Japan rebuild. p. 565	Japan rebuilt quickly and became a strong U.S. ally. p. 565
China	Mao Zedong defeated Chiang Kai-shek, signed the Sino-Soviet Pact (1950), and persecuted all anticommunists. pp. 569-70	The U.S. withdrew its limited military support of the Nationalists in 1947 and recognized Communist China in 1979. p. 570	The U.S. failed to stop the communists from taking over the world's most populous country. pp. 569-70

Skill: Synthesis

American Republic

Political Maps: The Presidential Election of 1948

The presidential election of 1948 is interesting for two reasons. First, newspapers chose the wrong winner. Second, the Democratic Party lost in the Deep South for the first time in seventy-two years (since Reconstruction).

Political maps help us to see how each region votes. Because the day begins three hours earlier in the East than the West, votes are counted there first. Since Dewey won the early votes, the papers assumed he would win.

Here are the raw data showing the electoral votes that each candidate won. Color the map on the next page with three colors to indicate which states each candidate won; then complete the pie graphs.

	Dewey	Truman	Thurmond
Maine	5		
New Hampshire	4		
Vermont	3		
Massachusetts		16	
Rhode Island		4	
Connecticut	8		
New York	47		
New Jersey	16		
Pennsylvania	35		
Delaware	3		
Maryland	8		
Ohio		25	
Michigan	19		
Indiana	13		
West Virginia		8	
Virginia		11	

	Dewey	Truman	Thurmond
North Carolina		14	
South Carolina			8
Georgia		12	
Florida		8	
Kentucky		11	
Tennessee		11	1
Alabama			11
Mississippi			9
Louisiana			10
Wisconsin		12	
Illinois		28	
Minnesota		11	
Iowa		10	
Missouri		15	
Arkansas		9	
North Dakota	4		

	Dewey	Truman	Thurmond
South Dakota	4		
Nebraska	6		
Kansas	8		
Oklahoma		10	
Texas		23	
Montana		4	
Wyoming		3	
Colorado		6	
New Mexico		4	
Utah		4	
Arizona		4	
Idaho		4	
Washington		8	
Oregon	6		
Nevada		3	
California		25	
Total	189	303	39

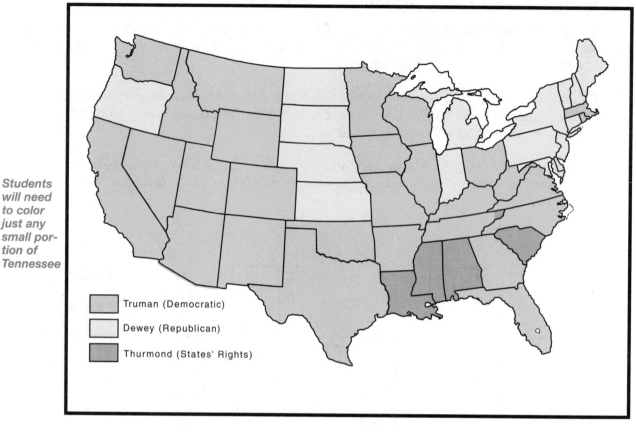

Students will need to color just any small portion of Tennessee

Truman (Democratic)

Dewey (Republican)

Thurmond (States' Rights)

Calculate the percentage (round to nearest half) of the total electoral vote that each candidate earned and then plot the percentages on the pie graph. (Hint: Don't forget to convert the percentages to degrees.)

Truman (Democrat) $303 \div 531 =$ __57__ %

Dewey (Republican) $189 \div 531 =$ __35.5__ %

Thurmond (States' Rights) $39 \div 531 =$ __7.5__ %

Calculate the percentage (round to nearest half) of the popular vote that each candidate received and plot the percentages on the pie graph. (Hint: Don't forget to convert the percentages to degrees.)

Truman (Democrat) $24{,}105{,}812 \div 48{,}687{,}608 =$ __49.5__ %

Dewey (Republican) $21{,}970{,}065 \div 48{,}687{,}608 =$ __45__ %

Thurmond (States' Rights) $1{,}169{,}021 \div 48{,}687{,}608 =$ __2.5__ %

Others $1{,}442{,}710 \div 48{,}687{,}608 =$ __3__ %

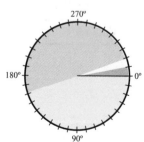

American Republic

Chapter 27   Activity D

Geography of the Postwar World

Following World War II, Americans could no longer afford to be ignorant of geography. Here are a few of the nations mentioned in this chapter. Match the nations with the descriptions. (Nations can be used more than once; some descriptions have more than one answer.)

A. United States
B. Canada
C. Cuba
D. Britain
E. France

F. Germany
G. Hungary
H. Soviet Union
I. China

J. Korea
K. Vietnam
L. Japan
M. Australia

_A, B, C_	1. located in the Western Hemisphere
_D, E, F, G, H_	2. located in Europe
_H, I, J, K, L_	3. located in Asia
_F, I, J, K_	4. divided into two nations by communists and the free world *pp. 568, 572*
_C, G, H_	5. communist nation (not divided) *pp. 564, 573-74*
_A, B, D, E, L, M_	6. free world nation (not divided) *pp. 565, 569, 572*
_F_	7. site of the Nuremburg trials *p. 564*
_F_	8. site of the Berlin airlift *pp. 568-69*
_L_	9. temporarily governed by General MacArthur *p. 564*
_A, D, E, H, I_	10. permanent member of the U.N. Security Council *p. 566*
_A, B, D, E (F)_	11. member of the North Atlantic Treaty Organization (NATO) *p. 569*
_G, H (F)_	12. member of the Warsaw Pact *pp. 569, 573*
_A, D, E, M_	13. member of the Southeast Asia Treaty Organization (SEATO) *p. 572*
_I_	14. civil war between Chiang Kai-shek and Mao Zedong *p. 569*
_C_	15. civil war between Fidel Castro and Fulgencio Batista *p. 574*
_J_	16. war between communists and U.N. troops *p. 571*
_K_	17. war between France and Ho Chi Minh *p. 572*
_G_	18. revolted against communist rule in 1956 *p. 573*
_H_	19. governed by Nikita Khrushchev *p. 573*
_A, B_	20. participated in the St. Lawrence Seaway project *p. 574*
_A_	21. admitted Alaska and Hawaii as new states in 1959 *p. 575*

American Republic

Chapter 28   Activity A

Time Line of the Sixties   ☆ *Classroom discussion*

For each topic below, choose the important events and place them in the *approximate* time period they occurred. (Note: The time line is two pages long.)

	1960	1961	1962	1963	1964
Presidency	Nixon-Kennedy debates p. 579; JFK's election p. 579		Congressional opposition to "Camelot" p. 582	JFK assassination p. 582; Johnson sworn in p. 582	
Domestic Programs		New Frontier p. 579; space program begins		The Great Society p. 582; "War on Poverty" p. 583	Job Corps p. 583; food stamps p. 583; Head Start p. 583
Civil Rights	integration of schools continues pp. 584-85; sit-ins p. 585	Twenty-third Amendment pp. 165, 585	enrollment of black students at the Univ. of Mississippi and Univ. of Alabama p. 585	Birmingham demonstration p. 585; march on Washington p. 585	"black power" p. 587; Twenty-fourth Amendment p. 586; Civil Rights Act p. 586
Foreign Programs		Peace Corps p. 580; Alliance for Progress p. 580			
Cold War		Bay of Pigs p. 581; Berlin Wall p. 580	Cuban Missile Crisis p. 581	"hot line" to Moscow p. 581; Limited Test Ban Treaty p. 582	
Vietnam		U.S. financial aid p. 588; U.S. advisory troops p. 588			Gulf of Tonkin Resolution p. 588

	1965	1966	1967	1968	1969
Presidency	Congressional cooperation with LBJ pp. 582-83			Robert Kennedy assassination p. 592 / Hubert Humphrey candidacy p. 592 / Nixon election p. 592	
Domestic Programs	Medicare p. 583 / Medicaid p. 583 / Department of Housing and Urban Development p. 583 / Department of Transportation p. 583		increasing national debt p. 583		
Civil Rights	Voting Rights Act p. 586 / urban riots begin (Watts) p. 587 / riots in Detroit and Newark p. 587			M. L. King Jr. assassination p. 587	
Foreign Programs					
Cold War	Chinese and Soviet aid to North Vietnam p. 589 / "New Left" agitation p. 590				
Vietnam	escalation of U.S. ground troops pp. 589-90 / antiwar demonstrations begin p. 590	bombing raids begin on North Vietnam p. 591		Tet Offensive p. 591	Vietnamization p. 593

Skill: Time Line

American Republic

News Segments from the Sixties and Early Seventies

During the 1960s, television began to overshadow radio and newspapers. Pretend you are a TV producer. You must write the script for three short news segments, each between thirty and ninety seconds. Each script has two parts: audio (spoken words, music, and sounds) and video (motion pictures, photographs, and printed material). Choose any three of the following events:

Nixon-Kennedy debates	Kennedy at Berlin Wall	bombing raids in Vietnam
Kennedy's inaugural speech	JFK's assassination	Tet Offensive
Bay of Pigs	Little Rock integration	Robert Kennedy's assassination
Cuban Missile Crisis	march on Washington	Johnson quits campaign
Berlin Wall's construction	city riots	Kent State shootings
Gulf of Tonkin incident	moon landing	Arab oil embargo
Roe v. Wade decision	resignation of Agnew	resignation of Nixon

Reporters used television not just to report history but to "make history" by shaping people's attitudes. After each segment, write what impact your report may have had on Americans.

Hint: To make your video more interesting, try some of these common techniques: fade in/out, zoom in/out, pan (panorama), cu (close up), ls (long shot).

Segment title __*Nixon-Kennedy Debates*__   Date __*1960*__

Director __*Example*__   Segment time __*:30*__

VIDEO	AUDIO
CLIPS FROM EACH DEBATE	*Tonight Kennedy and Nixon completed the last of their four debates.*
PAN START OF LAST DEBATE	*Both men knew their election might be riding on their performances.*
ZOOM IN KENNEDY	*But Kennedy, who started as the underdog, has had the most to*
	gain. He has proved his competence and charm.
CUT TO CU OF NIXON	*Nixon, on the other hand, seemed to lack energy and appeal.*
CUT TO FINAL HANDSHAKE	*November will show the real winner of the debates.*
CLIPS FROM CONVENTION RALLIES	*Who can tell whether the new president will win because of style*
PHOTO OF WHITE HOUSE	*or substance?*

Impact of report __*The TV reports often emphasized Kennedy's charm without telling viewers the substance of each candidate's speech. Liberal TV reporters selected the details that would improve Kennedy's image.*__

Segment title_____ Date _____

Director_____ Segment time _____

VIDEO   AUDIO

_____   _____

_____   _____

_____   _____

_____   _____

_____   _____

_____   _____

_____   _____

_____   _____

_____   _____

Impact of report_____

_____

_____

Segment title_____ Date _____

Director_____ Segment time _____

VIDEO   AUDIO

_____   _____

_____   _____

_____   _____

_____   _____

_____   _____

_____   _____

_____   _____

_____   _____

Impact of report_____

_____

_____

American Republic

Chapter 28   Activity C

Summary of the Vietnam War

The Vietnam War was the longest and least successful war in American history. To answer these questions about its significance, refer to your text, pages 572-73 and 588-94.

1. What country controlled Indochina before World War II? *France   p. 572*

2. What communist leader fought for Vietnamese independence? *Ho Chi Minh   p. 572*

3. What important victory did the communists win in 1954? *Dien Bien Phu   p. 572*

4. Why did the United States fail to intervene at this time? *The U.S. did not want to risk another land war like Korea.   p. 572*

5. How did the international conference in Geneva try to settle the conflict? *The country would be divided in half, giving North Vietnam to the communists.   p. 572*

6. Why did this settlement fail? *Not content, North Vietnam initiated guerrilla warfare in South Vietnam.   p. 572*

7. What two communist countries began sending military aid to North Vietnam? *China and the Soviet Union   p. 572*

8. What alliance did the U.S. join in 1954 to contain communism in Asia? *SEATO   p. 572*

9. When did the U.S. begin sending military advisors to South Vietnam? *1955   p. 573*

10. What was the purpose of sending these advisors? *They trained Vietnamese forces.   p. 573*

11. Who was the president at this time? *Eisenhower   pp. 572-73*

12. The Gulf of Tonkin Resolution authorized "all necessary steps" to stop North Vietnamese aggression.

    • What year was the resolution passed? *1964   p. 588*

    • Who was the president at the time? *Johnson   p. 588*

    • What incident sparked the resolution? *North Vietnamese patrols attacked two American destroyers in international waters off the coast of Vietnam.   p. 588*

13. List four disadvantages the United States faced during the conflict.

    Vietnamese politics was corrupt; the South Vietnamese were not united; Congress never declared war or gave a cause to rally public support; the terrain and scattered industry made it difficult for the U.S. to use its sophisticated weapons; the enemy was not easy to distinguish from the allies; the antiwar movement undermined the war effort.   pp. 589-90

14. What name was given to those who opposed the war? *doves   p. 588*

15. How many troops had been sent to Vietnam by May of 1965? *over half a million   pp. 588-89*

16. What term describes communist supporters living in South Vietnam? *Vietcong   p. 589*

17. What trail did North Vietnam use to supply the southern rebels? _Ho Chi Minh Trail_   _p. 589_

18. What was the capital of South Vietnam? _Saigon   p. 591_

19. How did Johnson attempt to hinder Soviet aid to North Vietnam? _bombing raids   p. 591_

20. What communist offensive caught Americans by surprise in 1968? _Tet   p. 591_

21. How did the media encourage opposition to the war? _In addition to displaying nightly_
    scenes of death, deceitful reporting about the Tet "defeat" made Americans eager to
    leave the war.   p. 591

22. Why did politicians begin to push for an end to the war in 1968? _Americans began to_
    have second thoughts about the war after Tet, so support for the war became a political
    liability. The escalation of the war ruined Johnson's political career.   pp. 591-92

23. Describe Nixon's plan to pull American troops out of Vietnam "with dignity."_____
    Vietnamization meant that the responsibility for fighting would gradually be returned to
    the South Vietnamese. The U.S. would continue sending supplies and making air attacks.
    _p. 593_

24. What steps did Nixon take to force North Vietnam to the peace table? _He expanded the_
    war into Cambodia in 1970 and into Laos in 1971. He increased the number of air strikes.
    He also had North Vietnamese waters mined.   p. 593

25. During what year did North Vietnam agree to a ceasefire? _1973   p. 593_

26. Who was president of the U.S. when North Vietnam violated the ceasefire in 1975? _Ford   p. 594_

27. In what year did South Vietnam fall? _1975   p. 594_

28. Name three ways that this war differed from earlier wars. _The war was never official; the_
    public never had a cause to support; antiwar riots were common; treason and dissent
    were tolerated and cheered; America lost; the press had few restrictions; veterans were
    ignored; Americans did not sacrifice domestic spending to pay for the war.

29. Name three ways the war hurt America. _Antiwar riots divided the nation; mistreatment of_
    the veterans caused bitterness; the reputation of the U.S. plummeted because the U.S.
    deserted its ally, South Vietnam; more than 50,000 young men were killed in a "no-win"
    war; the government debt exploded; Americans lost confidence in their leaders.

American Republic

Chapter 28   Activity D

Evaluating What You Read ☆ *Classroom discussion*

Many people do not believe the Christian perspective presented in your textbook. For each event below, write a brief defense from the supporter's perspective. Then, with the help of your book and your knowledge of Scripture, write what you think is wrong with this position.

1. Kennedy introduced the Peace Corps to improve conditions in third-world countries.

   Defense by a Peace Corps volunteer: *If people volunteer their talents to serve others,* *we can make the world a better place. We have the skills to improve schooling, health,* *and conservation in countries that cannot help themselves.*

   Christian evaluation of the Peace Corps (see p. 580): *Although helping the poor and needy* *is good, the Corps provided no permanent solutions. People have a spiritual need that* *only the Lord can satisfy.*

2. Kennedy announced the Alliance for Progress to ease communist unrest in Latin America.

   Defense by John F. Kennedy: *By helping Latin Americans build houses, schools, and* *health clinics, poor people will be less interested in the communist message.*

   Christian evaluation of the Alliance for Progress (see p. 580): *Money cannot improve* *people's minds and hearts. Expensive government aid encourages corruption.*

3. Lyndon Johnson introduced "The Great Society" to solve America's domestic problems.

   Defense by Lyndon Johnson: *We have the money and the talent to fight a "war on* *poverty" and to end the ills of our society. We can supply the poor with nutritious food,* *early education, medical care, and housing.*

   Christian evaluation of "The Great Society" (see pp. 582-83, 592): *The Great Society* *programs required deficit spending. These programs also made Americans dependent* *on government instead of God to meet their needs.*

4. Martin Luther King Jr. encouraged social action to liberate the poor and underprivileged.

Defense by King: *The gospel teaches that the poor and underprivileged peoples of this world should be free. Christians have a duty to bring liberty and justice to the world.*

Christian perspective of social action (see p. 587): *King did not preach the true gospel. Although his aims were noble, he was using methods such as civil disobedience that are not taught in Scripture.*

5. Stokely Carmichael advocated "black power" to solve racial inequality.

Defense by Carmichael: *"Violence is as American as cherry pie," according to Carmichael. Racial inequality is wrong, so we have a right to use force to right this wrong.*

Christian perspective on "black power" (see p. 587): *Violence is clearly offensive to God. Extremists caused more harm than good, setting back the civil rights movement by alienating potential supporters.*

6. The antiwar movement attempted to undermine the war effort.

Defense by liberal college professor: *The capitalist American government is killing innocent people to further its evil ends. Conscientious citizens have a duty to undermine this evil.*

Christian perspective on the antiwar movement (see p. 590): *American demonstrators promoted rebellion against their own God-instituted government. (Their opposition to the war indirectly helped a ruthless government take over South Vietnam and murder perhaps millions.)*

7. The evening news carried nightly scenes of blood and death in Vietnam.

Defense by a newscaster: *People have a right to know what is happening in the world. We are showing Americans war as it really is.*

Christian perspective on the role of media (see p. 591): *The liberal media helped undermine the war effort. Newscasters can manipulate people by the way they censor the news. For example, the media reported the Tet Offensive as a miserable defeat without mentioning the American successes.*

Skill: Evaluation

American Republic

Chapter 29   Activity A

The Cost of Federal Bureaucracy    *Classroom discussion*

The explosive growth of federal government hurt the economy in many ways. Here are some related problems that concerned Americans in the 1980s. You may use your calculator to solve them.

The U.S. exported $43 billion worth of merchandise in 1970 and imported $40 billion. In 1990 it exported $394 billion and imported $495 billion.

1. How much did the value of exports increase between 1970 and 1990? *$351 billion*

2. How much did the value of imports increase between 1970 and 1990? *$455 billion*

3. What trade balance (exports minus imports) did the U.S. enjoy in 1970? *$3 billion*

4. What negative trade balance did the U.S. suffer in 1990? *$101 billion*

This chart shows the federal government's total debt (in billions of dollars) from the start of World War II to 1990.

Year	1940	1945	1950	1955	1960	1965	1970	1975	1980	1985	1990
National Debt	43	259	256	273	284	314	370	533	908	1823	3233

5. How much did the debt grow during World War II (from 1940 to 1945)? *$216 billion*

6. How much did the debt grow during the postwar era (from 1945 to 1960)? *$25 billion*

7. How much did the debt grow after the New Frontier (1960 to 1990)? *$2,949 billion*

8. Interest on the debt was about 3% in 1960. How much interest did the government pay on the debt that year (national debt x 0.03)? *$8.5 billion*

9. Interest on the debt was about 8% in 1990. How much interest did the government pay on the debt that year? *$259 billion*

10. The federal government spent $77 billion in 1960. What percentage of its expenses was interest on the national debt? *11%*

11. The federal government spent $1,252 billion in 1990. What percentage of its expenses was interest on the national debt? *21%*

Extra Challenge: The chart on page 607 shows how rapidly prices rose during the 1970s. The following questions help you to see how much this inflation raised the cost of living.

12. Inflation was 12.2% in 1974. How much did goods worth $100 at the beginning of the year cost at the end of the year? *$112.20*

13. Prices rose 110% between 1970 and 1980. How much did goods worth $100 at the beginning of the 1970s cost at the end of the decade? *$210*

14. Inflation reached a new high in Carter's last year in office (1980). If you had $113.50 at the beginning of the year, you could buy only $100 worth of goods at the end of the year. What was the inflation rate? *13.5%*

Picture Graphs

Refer to the first page of this activity to make the picture graphs. You may use a row of money bags or dollar signs ($) as the symbol for money. Round up or down to nearest whole symbol.

National Debt: What was the total national debt each year ($100 billion per money symbol)?

1960 $ $ $ *(2.8 bags)*

1990 $ *(32.3 bags)*

Interest on the Debt: What was the interest on the national debt each year ($10 billion/symbol)?

1960 $ *(0.9 bags)*

1990 $ *(25.9 bags)*

Federal Spending: How much did the federal government spend each year ($100 billion/symbol)?

1960 $ *(0.8 bags)*

1990 $ $ $ $ $ $ $ $ $ $ $ $ *(12.5 bags)*

Trade Balance: What were the total imports and exports each year ($40 billion/symbol)?

1970 Imports $ *(1 bag)*

1970 Exports $ *(1 bag)*

1990 Imports $ $ $ $ $ $ $ $ $ $ $ *(12.4 bags)*

1990 Exports $ $ $ $ $ $ $ $ $ *(10 bags)*

American Republic

Chapter 29   Activity B

Lessons from Bad News   ☆ *Classroom discussion*

Christians should not fret about "bad news." God has a purpose for all things, "a time to weep, and a time to laugh" (Eccles. 3:4). The events of the 1970s forced Americans to question the nation's departure from its conservative roots. By applying the lessons they had learned, Americans had an opportunity to make the nation stronger in the 1980s. Give the specifics (five *W*s) of each event below. (You will need to refer to both Chapters 28 and 29.) Then write one lesson that the event taught or one "good" result.

1. The president seeks friendly relations with communist countries. *With Kissinger's help, Nixon brought in a new era of détente. In 1972 Nixon visited the Soviet Union to discuss a Strategic Arms Limitations Treaty, even though communists had a reputation of deceit.   p. 595*

   Lesson *"Conservatives" are not always conservative. Reagan sought to improve the national defense so that he could negotiate with the Soviet Union from a stronger position.   pp. 595-96, 613-14*

2. The vice president resigns. *Spiro T. Agnew was charged with accepting bribes and with evading income tax, to which he pleaded no contest. Facing a possible prison sentence, he resigned on October 10, 1973.   p. 600*

   Lesson *No one is above the law. The Twenty-fifth Amendment gives guidelines for presidential succession during a crisis.   p. 600*

3. The president resigns. *When Congress threatened to impeach Nixon over his involvement in the Watergate conspiracy, Nixon resigned on August 9, 1974. Tapes of his office conversations revealed that the president knew about the burglary and attempted to stop an FBI investigation.   pp. 600-601*

   Lesson *The Constitution's system of checks and balances still works. Congress strengthened the Freedom of Information Act and passed a Federal Campaign Reform Act.   pp. 601-2*

4. The nation suffers "double-digit" inflation. *Under Carter, annual inflation rates rose above ten percent, and interest rates surged. As a result, the economy floundered. Like Ford's WIN, Carter asked people to accept voluntary wage and price controls.   p. 607*

   Lesson *Inflation is caused by the government, not people. Reagan promised to cut inflation by returning to a classical free-enterprise system, often referred to as "supply-side economics."   pp. 611-12*

5. The price of crude oil skyrockets. *To protest America's support of Israel, OPEC ordered an oil embargo in October 1973, leading to an energy crisis. Prices of oil products rose dramatically until OPEC countries split over production limits and prices.   pp. 598, 608*

   Lesson *Realizing the danger of relying on foreign oil, Americans began to conserve energy and to develop alternative energy sources. Carter proposed deregulation of price controls.   p. 608*

6. The courts legalize abortion. _Even with conservatives in the Supreme Court, the justices_ _decided in 1973 that a woman has the right to abort her unborn child. Since then, about_ _one-third of all American babies (1.5 million) have been legally murdered each year._ *p. 598*

Lesson _"Conservative" courts are not always conservative. Reagan attempted to shape the_ _Supreme Court into a more conservative force. Christians need to pray for the justices' decisions._ *p. 612*

7. South Vietnam falls. _When North Vietnam violated its ceasefire, Congress refused to_ _increase aid to South Vietnam. The last American troops left Saigon in the spring of 1975,_ _and the South Vietnamese surrendered within two weeks._ *p. 594*

Lesson _Communists cannot be trusted. Their military capabilities shouldn't be underesti-_ _mated. An unrestricted press can manipulate public opinion and shape military policy._ *p. 594*

8. The Soviets invade Afghanistan. _Claiming they were invited, the Soviet Union invaded_ _Afghanistan in 1979 and set up a puppet regime. Carter's punishment, a boycott of the_ _1980 Olympic Games, was weak._ *pp. 609-10*

Lesson _Détente came to an end. Reagan made a tough stand against the "evil empire." He_ _promoted "Star Wars" and a strong national defense._ *pp. 613-14*

9. Radical Arabs take Americans hostage. _On November 4, 1979, a group of Iranian students_ _connected with the Ayatollah Khomeini took sixty-six Americans hostage. Iranians were_ _retaliating for America's aid to the shah. The hostages were finally freed after 444 days._ *p. 610*

Lesson _Americans were humiliated by feeble responses to terrorists. Reagan bombed the_ _terrorist supporter Qaddafi. Reagan officially opposed bargaining with terrorists._ *pp. 614-15*

10. America gives up control of canal. _When Carter resumed negotiations with Panama to_ _renew America's lease, he signed a new Panama Canal Treaty (1977) that transferred_ _control of the Canal Zone in 1999. The Senate approved the treaty after heated debate._ *p. 608*

Lesson _Many Americans believed we had given up something of value too easily. Bush_ _asserted America's interest in the region by invading Panama in 1989 to depose Noriega._ *pp. 608-9, 617*

11. Communist government is set up in Central America. _Before Reagan took office, the_ _Sandinistas, with Cuban aid, had set up a communist government in Nicaragua. This_ _situation raised fears that communist-backed revolution would spread in the region._ *pp. 614-15*

Lesson _Reagan invaded Grenada to show his determination to stop the spread of commu-_ _nism, and he channeled support to the Contras in Nicaragua._ *pp. 614-15*

American Republic

Chapter 29   Activity C

Presents after Nixon

Match the presidents with the phrases that are *best* associated with them.

A. Gerald Ford
B. Jimmy Carter
C. Ronald Reagan
D. George Bush

_B_ 1. peanut farmer *p. 607*

_C_ 2. actor and broadcaster *p. 611*

_A_ 3. college football star *p. 605*

_B_ 4. governor of Georgia *p. 606*

_C_ 5. reelected by a landslide *p. 613*

_B_ 6. Iranian hostage crisis *p. 610*

_A_ 7. never elected to office *pp. 604-5*

_A_ 8. pardoned Nixon *p. 605*

_B_ 9. offered amnesty to draft dodgers *p. 607*

_B_ 10. Three Mile Island *p. 608*

_C_ 11. Rehnquist court *p. 612*

_A_ 12. Bicentennial *p. 604*

_C_ 13. Iran-Contra Affair *p. 615*

_D_ 14. S&L bankruptcies *p. 618*

_D_ 15. collapse of the Soviet Union *p. 617*

_D_ 16. protest at Tiananmen Square *p. 617*

_B_ 17. 1979 energy crisis *p. 608*

_D_ 18. first vice president elected president since 1836 *p. 616*

_C_ 19. bombing of Libya *p. 614*

_B_ 20. Soviet invasion of Afghanistan *p. 609*

_D_ 21. invasion of Panama *p. 617*

_C_ 22. invasion of Grenada *p. 614*

_D_ 23. Persian Gulf War *p. 617*

_C_ 24. Intermediate Nuclear Forces Treaty *p. 614*

_B_ 25. Panama Canal Treaty *p. 608*

_D_ 26. START *p. 617*

_B_ 27. SALT II *p. 609*

_B_ 28. Camp David Accords *p. 609*

_C_ 29. Republican-controlled Senate *p. 611*

_C_ 30. largest income-tax cut in U.S. history *p. 612*

_D_ 31. 1990 budget deal *p. 621*

_C_ 32. "Star Wars" program *pp. 613-14*

_A_ 33. WIN anti-inflation crusade *p. 605*

_C_ 34. supply-side economics *p. 612*

_D_ 35. Americans with Disabilities Act *p. 619*

American Republic

Chapter 30   Activity A

Current Events

The issues that you have studied in your text are still being discussed today. Find a current reference to each topic below. Write the magazine or newspaper you found it in, the date, the title of the article, and what the article said about this topic.

Economy

Magazine _____ Date _____

Title _____

Summary _____

_____

Budget

Magazine _____ Date _____

Title _____

Summary _____

_____

Welfare reform

Magazine _____ Date _____

Title _____

Summary _____

_____

Health care

Magazine _____ Date _____

Title _____

Summary _____

_____

Education

Magazine _____ Date _____

Title _____

Summary _____

_____

Breakdown of the family

Magazine_____ Date _____

Title_____

Summary_____

_____

Abortion

Magazine_____ Date _____

Title_____

Summary_____

_____

Homosexual rights

Magazine_____ Date _____

Title_____

Summary_____

_____

Communications technology

Magazine_____ Date _____

Title_____

Summary_____

_____

Role of NATO

Magazine_____ Date _____

Title_____

Summary_____

_____

Trade disputes

Magazine_____ Date _____

Title_____

Summary_____

_____

Skill: Writing

American Republic

How Clinton Lost the Health Care Debate

Americans already enjoy the best health care in the world, so they fear changes. The secrecy that surrounded the preparation of Clinton's health-care plan only inflamed their fears. Democrats tried to present the plan in the best light, but Americans were not deceived. Read each statement and the truth behind it. Match the best label for each example of faulty reasoning.

A. hasty generalization from little evidence
B. appeal to emotions, such as fear, pity, shame, or national pride
C. suppressed (or withheld) evidence
D. false dichotomy (limiting choices to "either . . . or")

___C___ 1. Clinton said 15 percent of Americans (thirty-eight million) do not have health insurance. But he did not mention that most were temporary cases involving healthy young people. Only 3 percent (six million) were unwillingly uninsured for a long time.

___B___ 2. Clinton chided America because foreign health care is "cheaper." He wanted Americans to be ashamed of their system, even though health care in the U.S. is the envy of the world.

___D___ 3. Clinton said that his reforms were the only way to keep health care from becoming 28 percent of the federal budget by the year 2002. But without his plan, costs began to drop.

___B___ 4. Clinton said this rich nation has a moral obligation to give all citizens "security of mind" about health care. But his wording made Clinton's opponents appear heartless.

___C___ 5. Clinton said his system was "streamlined and simpler." But he did not show the details. Opponents to Clinton's system said the plan would "create fifty-nine new federal programs or bureaucracies, expand twenty others, impose seventy-nine new federal mandates, and make major changes in the tax code."

___A___ 6. Clinton said he would "pay" for reform through savings generated by less paperwork and increased efficiency. But he had little basis for this claim. His system had never been tested.

___C___ 7. Clinton said he would not raise taxes, except on cigarettes. But he did not acknowledge that forcing businesses to pay insurance premiums is a "tax" that, according to the Congressional Budget Office, would cost businesses hundreds of billions of dollars.

American Republic

Chapter 30   Activity C

What God Says About Modern Issues

The Scriptures tell us all we need to know about "modern" issues. One modern belief is that mankind can solve his own problems. Look up each Scripture passage and place its letter in the blank beside the truth that Scripture teaches.

A. Genesis 3:16-19
B. Ecclesiastes 1:15
C. Ecclesiastes 3:19-20
D. Luke 12:15
E. John 14:27

F. Ephesians 2:1-3
G. Ephesians 2:8
H. Ephesians 2:11-12
I. I Timothy 6:6-8
J. II Timothy 3:1, 7

__A__ 1. God has placed a curse on this world so that man must always live in sorrow.

__J__ 2. People in the end times will be constantly learning but never able to find the truth.

__E__ 3. The world does not give lasting peace.

__B__ 4. Mankind cannot straighten all that is crooked or supply all that is lacking.

__H__ 5. Without Christ we have no hope.

__C__ 6. All men, like beasts, will one day return to dust.

__F__ 7. All people are dead and ruled by Satan until Christ gives them life.

__G__ 8. No one can save himself; salvation is a gift of God.

__D__ 9. A man's life consists not in the abundance of his possessions.

__I__ 10. True wealth comes from godliness and contentment.

Modern Americans reject absolute moral standards, yet they advocate various "human rights." Look up these verses. What do they teach about human rights and responsibilities?

11. Jeremiah 22:3 _God expects the government (here, the king) to treat its citizens with_ _justice._

12. Matthew 12:36-37 _In the day of judgment, God will judge every idle word that people_ _have spoken._

13. Mark 7:20-23 _Evil things come from within, out of the heart of people. Since the_ _government cannot change hearts, the solution to evil is spiritual conversion._

14. John 8:31-36 _True freedom is freedom from sin's control. This freedom comes through_ _obedience to Christ's Word. Our privilege is to serve God, not Satan._

15. John 12:48 _Christ's Word is the standard by which God will judge all people. His_ _standards are absolute._

Name _____

American Republic

Chapter 30   Activity D

Modern Conveniences in Your Home

Scientific advances are constantly changing the way we live. With the help of an adult in your family, complete this survey of your home.

1. Do you know someone who has benefited from any of these modern medical advances? Write your relationship to the person in the blank.

   ❑ artificial limb_____
   ❑ heart pacemaker_____
   ❑ scratch-proof glasses_____
   ❑ other_____

2. Does your kitchen include any of these modern conveniences? Give a brief description of one.

   ❑ microwave oven_____
   ❑ cordless mixer_____
   ❑ food processor_____
   ❑ self-cleaning oven_____
   ❑ stick-free pots and pans_____
   ❑ dishwasher_____
   ❑ other_____

3. Does your house have any of these modern tools and supplies?

   ❑ cordless tools
   ❑ electronic level
   ❑ polyurethane
   ❑ rechargeable flashlight
   ❑ cordless vacuum cleaner
   ❑ other_____

4. Does your family have any of these electronic conveniences? Give a brief description of one.

   ❑ electronic scales_____
   ❑ electronic clock_____
   ❑ compact disc player_____
   ❑ color television_____
   ❑ electronic keyboard_____
   ❑ computer_____

© 2000 BJU Press. Reproduction prohibited.

❏ VCR_____

❏ camcorder_____

❏ fax machine_____

❏ answering machine_____

❏ phone with memory_____

❏ cellular phone_____

❏ automatic 35mm camera_____

❏ other_____

5. Do *you* have any of these modern conveniences? Give a brief description of one.

❏ synthetic clothing_____

❏ electronic watch_____

❏ portable radio_____

❏ computerized game_____

❏ laser toy_____

❏ robotic toy_____

❏ calculator_____

❏ other_____

6. Choose five modern conveniences from the lists above. Describe what people used to do without them.

_____

_____

_____

_____

_____

7. Bonus: Choose one convenience from the lists above. Give a brief history of its development.

_____

_____

_____

_____

_____

_____

_____

_____

American Republic

Chapter 30   Activity E

Comparing Clinton to a Past Democratic President ☆ *Classroom discussion*

You may want to assign just one president but discuss all four in class.

Both friends and enemies of Bill Clinton liked to compare him to his Democratic predecessors—especially Franklin D. Roosevelt, Harry S. Truman, John F. Kennedy, and Jimmy Carter. Choose one of these men. Then find Clinton's similarities and differences.

Name	*Answers will vary.*	**Bill Clinton**
Occupation		*attorney p. 625*
Hometown		*Little Rock, Arkansas p. 625*
Religion		*Southern Baptist p. 625*
Character Reputation		*adulterer; draft dodger; drug user p. 624*
Role of First Lady		*politically active; headed health-care task force p. 627*
Success in Getting Legislation Passed		*passage of old legislation (NAFTA, Brady Bill, Medical Leave); failure to reform health care; grudging signature of Republican welfare reform and telecommunications deregulation pp. 627-28, 634*
New Social Policies		*"children's rights"; homosexual and abortion rights (including FACE bill and partial birth abortions); Goals 2000 pp. 625-26, 634-35*
New Taxes		*record-breaking increase in taxes p. 627*
New Bureaucracy (Government Programs)		*proposed socialized health care, AmeriCorps pp. 627-28*
New Regulation of Business		*new environmental regulations; Medical Leave Act p. 627*
Popularity		*amazingly high job-approval ratings during the impeachment (although character ratings were at record lows) pp. 625, 639*
Scandals		*cabinet investigations; Whitewater; campaign financing; sex scandals (Paula Jones, Monica Lewinsky) pp. 637-39*
Approach Toward the United Nations		*expanded UN peacekeeping; multilateralism p. 642*
Major Challenges in Foreign Relations		*post-Cold War problems; cuts and low morale in the military; catastrophe in Somalia; invasion of Haiti; waffling on Bosnia; air war in Kosovo; NAFTA; GATT pp. 639-44*

Chapter Review

Skill: Charts   **189**

American Republic

Supplement   Activity A

Eras of American History

Complete the chart on the reverse side. First, place the *eras* of American history in chronological order. Then place the *people, events,* and *terms* beside the eras with which they are most closely associated.

Eras

Civil War
Cold War
colonial settlement
Confederation
Depression
exploration of America
Good Feelings

imperialism
Jacksonian Democracy
last frontier
Manifest Destiny
new federal government
progressivism

Reconstruction
Roaring Twenties
War for Independence
War of 1812
World War I
World War II

People

William Bradford
Al Capone
Christopher Columbus
George A. Custer
George III
Alexander Hamilton
Adolf Hitler

Andrew Jackson
Andrew Johnson
Abraham Lincoln
James Madison
William McKinley
James Monroe

Franklin D. Roosevelt
Theodore Roosevelt
Winfield Scott
Daniel Shays
Harry S. Truman
Woodrow Wilson

Events

attack on Pearl Harbor
battle of Gettysburg
battle of New Orleans
battle of Yorktown
black codes
Fourteen Points
Homestead Act

Korean War
Line of Demarcation
Mayflower Compact
Mexican War
Missouri Compromise
Northwest Ordinance

nullification controversy
Pure Food and Drug Act
Social Security
Spanish-American War
Teapot Dome Scandal
Washington's inauguration

Terms

blitzkrieg
blockade runners
cabinet system
carpetbaggers
conquistadors
containment
doughboys

Dust Bowl
flappers
forty-niners
Loyalists
party caucus
Puritans

referendums
Sooners
spoils system
square townships
War Hawks
yellow journalism

Era	Person	Event	Term
exploration of America	Christopher Columbus p. 4	Line of Demarcation p. 6	conquistadors p. 5
colonial settlement	William Bradford p. 19	Mayflower Compact p. 19	Puritans p. 18
War for Independence	George III p. 84	battle of Yorktown p. 108	Loyalists p. 98
Confederation	Daniel Shays p. 120	Northwest Ordinance p. 114	square townships p. 115
new federal government	Alexander Hamilton p. 171	Washington's inauguration p. 170	cabinet system p. 171
War of 1812	James Madison p. 206	battle of New Orleans p. 212	War Hawks p. 208
Good Feelings	James Monroe p. 219	Missouri Compromise p. 225	party caucus p. 219
Jacksonian Democracy	Andrew Jackson p. 234	nullification controversy pp. 239-42	spoils system p. 236
Manifest Destiny	Winfield Scott p. 298	Mexican War p. 296	forty-niners p. 304
Civil War	Abraham Lincoln p. 323	battle of Gettysburg p. 347	blockade runners p. 342
Reconstruction	Andrew Johnson p. 363	black codes p. 364	carpetbaggers p. 368
last frontier	George A. Custer p. 424	Homestead Act p. 419	Sooners p. 420
imperialism	William McKinley p. 436	Spanish-American War p. 435	yellow journalism p. 436
progressivism	Theodore Roosevelt p. 463	Pure Food and Drug Act p. 461	referendums p. 462
World War I	Woodrow Wilson p. 490	Fourteen Points p. 490	doughboys p. 487
Roaring Twenties	Al Capone p. 505	Teapot Dome Scandal p. 509	flappers p. 502
Depression	Franklin D. Roosevelt p. 522	Social Security p. 527	Dust Bowl p. 519
World War II	Adolf Hitler p. 534	attack on Pearl Harbor p. 541	blitzkrieg p. 537
Cold War	Harry S. Truman p. 568	Korean War p. 571	containment p. 568

American Republic

The Presidents

Match each president with the phrase most closely associated with his administration.

A. Washington
B. John Adams
C. Jefferson
D. Madison
E. Monroe
F. John Q. Adams
G. Jackson
H. Van Buren
I. William H. Harrison
J. Tyler
K. Polk
L. Taylor
M. Fillmore
N. Pierce

O. Buchanan
P. Lincoln
Q. Andrew Johnson
R. Grant
S. Hayes
T. Garfield
U. Arthur
V. Cleveland
W. Benjamin Harrison
X. McKinley
Y. Theodore Roosevelt
Z. Taft
AB. Wilson
AC. Harding

AD. Coolidge
AE. Hoover
AF. Franklin D. Roosevelt
AG. Truman
AH. Eisenhower
AI. Kennedy
AJ. Lyndon B. Johnson
AK. Nixon
AL. Ford
AM. Carter
AN. Reagan
AO. Bush
AP. Clinton

__AI__ 1. Cuban missile crisis *p. 581*

__AM__ 2. Iranian hostage crisis *p. 610*

__R__ 3. scandals of Radical Reconstruction *p. 372*

__AE__ 4. stock market crash of 1929 *p. 514*

__AC__ 5. Teapot Dome Scandal *p. 509*

__AK__ 6. Watergate *p. 600*

__AG__ 7. Korean War *p. 571*

__K__ 8. Mexican War *p. 296*

__AO__ 9. Persian Gulf War *p. 617*

__X__ 10. Spanish-American War *p. 435*

__D__ 11. War of 1812 *pp. 206-8*

__Y__ 12. "big stick" policy *p. 444*

__Z__ 13. dollar diplomacy *p. 445*

__AJ__ 14. The Great Society *p. 582*

__AF__ 15. New Deal *p. 522*

__AH__ 16. peaceful coexistence *p. 573*

__G__ 17. spoils system *p. 236*

__AN__ 18. supply-side economics *p. 612*

__A__ 19. first president *p. 170*

__L__ 20. hero of Buena Vista who died in office *pp. 305-6*

__B__ 21. Alien and Sedition Acts *p. 186*

__M__ 22. Compromise of 1850 *p. 306*

__O__ 23. Dred Scott decision *p. 320*

__P__ 24. Emancipation Proclamation *p. 348*

__U__ 25. Exclusion Act of 1882 *p. 392*

__AB__ 26. Fourteen Points *p. 490*

__H__ 27. independent treasury *p. 247*

__C__ 28. Louisiana Purchase *p. 198*

__W__ 29. Oklahoma land rush *p. 420*

__AD__ 30. stock market speculation *p. 509*

__F__ 31. tariff of abominations *p. 228*

__E__ 32. Era of Good Feelings *p. 219*

__S__ 33. Bourbon Reconstruction *pp. 373-74*

__AL__ 34. never elected to office *p. 605*

__Q__ 35. first president to be impeached *p. 370*

__AP__ 36. impeached as a result of a sex scandal *pp. 638-39*

__V__ 37. two nonconsecutive terms *p. 418*

__N__ 38. Doughface *p. 306*

__T__ 39. assassinated by an office seeker *p. 391*

__J__ 40. man without a party *p. 249*

__I__ 41. Tippecanoe; died after one month in office *pp. 247-48*

American Republic

Map Study: The States and Their Capitals

Label all fifty states and their capitals.

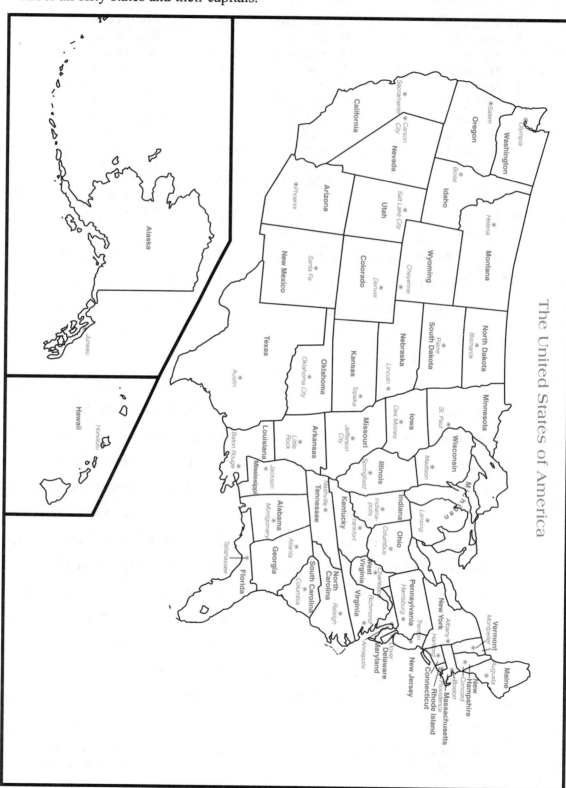

The United States of America

      Skill: Maps

American Republic

Supplement   Activity D

What If?    Classroom discussion

Here are some events that might have changed the course of American history. Based on what you have learned this year, describe how each different event might have changed America. Then tell why you believe God made each event turn out the way it did.

1. What if the Pilgrims had landed in Virginia, as planned? _The South may have_

   developed a completely different culture.   pp. 18-19, 28-29

   Why do you believe they sailed off course and landed at Plymouth, Massachusetts?

   God directed the Pilgrims to live in the North, where the soil is harsh. The North became

   a thriving center of trade.   pp. 20, 36-37

2. What if King George III had accepted the colonists' petition for taxation by their own representative bodies?

   The colonists may never have united for a War for Independence.   p. 82

   Why do you believe King George III replied, "The Colonies must either submit or triumph"?

   God gave the United States an opportunity to become a distinctive, independent nation.

   _p. 89_

3. What if the Anti-Federalists had prevented New York and Virginia from ratifying the Constitution?

   The United States may never have become a strong, united nation.   p. 129

   Why do you believe the Federalists won?

   God allowed the United States to become a strong republic.

4. What if President Thomas Jefferson had refused to make the Louisiana Purchase because the Constitution did not grant him the power to buy land?

   The United States may never have spread west of the Mississippi.   pp. 198-99

   Why do you believe Jefferson bought the land from France?

   God enabled the United States to grow and prosper. He prevented another nation from

   developing this region.

5. What if the South had seceded during the nullification controversy of 1832, when the South was equal to the North in population, money, and power?

The South may have won an earlier civil war and become an independent nation. The United States may have been permanently divided.   pp. 239-42

Why do you believe the sections agreed to the Compromise of 1833?

The time was not yet ripe for the Civil War. God waited until the South was not strong enough to win.

6. What if President Lincoln's guard had been present to prevent his assassination, allowing Lincoln to lead Reconstruction?

The century of southern hardships and bitterness may have been alleviated. The South may have blocked the introduction of civil rights measures.   pp. 362-70

Why do you believe Johnson became president, allowing the Radicals to lead?

The Lord allowed the South to endure great hardships. He allowed the power of the presidency to be tested but not broken.

7. What if the Allies had adopted President Wilson's "peace without victory" policy?

Germany's economy may have recovered from the war, and the world may have avoided the next world war.   pp. 490-92

Why do you believe the Allies imposed the harsh Treaty of Versailles, which ruined Germany's chance for recovery and bred support for the Nazi Party?

God allowed the world to suffer one of its greatest tragedies. Events disproved man's false hope of manmade peace.   p. 495

8. What if President Roosevelt had refused to recognize Stalin's "special interests" in Eastern Europe during World War II?

The communists may never have gained the power that they enjoyed at the outset of the Cold War.   pp. 546-47

Why do you believe the communists were allowed to take Eastern Europe and Berlin?

God allowed the communists to threaten the world and divide the West. He let the world see the evil and foolishness of communism.   pp. 567-68

9. What if President Truman had adopted an isolationist position after World War II?

Communism may have captured a majority of the nations, stopping the spread of the gospel and closing the free world market necessary for America's prosperity.   p. 568

Why do you believe America adopted the containment policy during the Cold War?

God allowed communism to grow, but only so far. He did not allow either side to win an easy victory.   pp. 568-72

Skill: Evaluation

American Republic

Supplement   Activity E

Changes in the United States: 1790s and Today

Here's your chance to be a history detective. How would you complete this fact sheet in 1790? What would you say now? Decide which resources to consult (almanac, textbook, encyclopedia, *U.S. Statistical Abstract,* or some other library resource). (Hint: Some blanks should say "none.")

Geography	1790	Today
1. Total land area	864,746 square miles	3,618,770 square miles
2. Number of states	13	50
3. Largest state	Virginia	Alaska
4. Frontier border	Appalachians	none
5. Largest city	Philadelphia	New York City
6. National capital	New York City	Washington, D.C.

Government	1790	Today
7. President	Washington	See almanac.
8. Secretary of State	Jefferson	See almanac.
9. Number of civilians in the federal government	fewer than one thousand	over three million
10. Age of the Constitution	one year	over 200 years
11. Major political parties	none (Federalist, Democratic-Republican)	Democratic Republican
12. Yearly government expenses	about $600 thousand	over $1.5 trillion
13. Total government debt	$75 million	over $5 trillion
14. Social Security tax rate	none	7.65%
15. Maximum income tax rate	none	39.6%

International Conditions	1790	Today
16. World population	less than 900 million	over 6 billion
17. World's richest nation	Great Britain	United States
18. Main international language	French	English
19. America's enemies	Indians, Gr. Brit., Fr., Sp.	Answers will vary.
20. America's main military alliance	none	NATO
21. America's most recent war	War for Independence	See almanac.

22. America's main trading partner(s)	Great Britain	Japan; Canada
23. Main import	manufactured goods	machinery
24. Main export	cash crops	machinery

Population

25. Total population	3,929,214	over 260 million
26. People in each square mile	4.5	over 70
27. Average (median) age	less than 16	about 35
28. Average life expectancy	about 35	about 77
29. Average family size	5.8	about 2.6

Daily Life

30. Total passenger cars	none	over 135 million
31. Total television sets	none	over 220 million
32. Total paved miles	less than one thousand	over four million
33. Fastest transportation	ship	jet (or rocket)
34. One major energy source	wind, water, or animals	oil, electricity, or nuclear
35. Last national revival	1740s	1860
36. One popular sport	hunting, racing	football, basketball, etc.
37. One popular music style	classical, folk	rock, rap
38. One popular hero	Washington	Answers will vary.
39. Leading cause of death	infection and disease	heart disease
40. Portrait on penny	no U.S. mint (sundial)	Lincoln

Discuss with students the disappearance of honorable heroes and the rise of evil musical styles. What do these changes say about our culture today?

Skill: Using Resources